Fast Foods *made* *Healthy*

High Cal Foods made Low Cal

[Also Includes a CALORIE COUNTER]

TARLA DALAL

India's # 1 Cookery Author

S&C
SANJAY & CO.
MUMBAI

Fourth Printing : 2005

Copyright © Sanjay & Co.

ISBN : 81-86469-75-3

All rights reserved with the publishers.

No part of this book may be reproduced, stored in a retrieval system or transmitted by any means, electronic, mechanical, photocopying, recording or otherwise, without the written permission of the publishers.

Price: Rs. 89/-

Published & Distributed by : **Sanjay & Company**

353/A-1, Shah & Nahar Industrial Estate, Dhanraj Mill Compound,
Lower Parel (W), Mumbai - 400 013. INDIA.
Tel. : (91-22) 2496 8068 ● Fax : (91-22) 2496 5876 ● E-mail : sanjay@tarladalal.com

Printed by : **Jupiter Prints**, Mumbai

Nutritionist	**Typesetting**	**Designed by**
Nisha Katira	Adityas Enterprises	Satyamangal Rege

DISCLAIMER

While every precaution has been taken in the preparation of this book, the publishers and the author assume no responsibility for errors or omissions. Neither is any liability assumed for damages resulting from the use of information contained herein. And of course, no book is a substitute for a qualified medical advice. So it is wiser to modify your dietary patterns under the supervision of a doctor or a nutritionist.

BULK PURCHASES

Tarla Dalal Cookbooks are ideal gifts. If you are interested in buying more than 500 assorted copies of Tarla Dalal Cookbooks at special prices, please contact us at 91-22-2496 8068 or email : sanjay@tarladalal.com

~ INTRODUCTION ~

Most of us regularly indulge in foods that are not very healthy. Pizzas, burgers, french fries, vada pav, heavy and rich curries and calorie laden sweets are all foods that can lure us away from the strictest diet. An occasional indulgence is not harmful but getting hooked is. For example, when we choose an aerated beverage instead of water almost everyday that's when we are heading towards steady weight gain.

The idea behind this book was to create appetizing low calorie versions of all our favourite foods…. pizzas, bhel, dal makhani, mayonnaise and many more…. Wouldn't it be wonderful if we could indulge in all such favourite foods and yet lose weight and remain trim? That's a dream for most of us today…..GUILT FREE EATING.

Keeping this in mind we need to cut down on calories, but not necessarily on fun that's associated with food. **I have selected some high calorie recipes which most of us indulge in on a regular basis and worked at making them low calorie yet keeping them as delicious as the original recipe.** Although the caloric difference between a few high cal and low cal recipes may not be very drastic, the low calorie recipes have certainly fewer calories contributed by fat, which is the most crucial cause for adding those extra inches to your waist.

You will discover that a few changes in the way we cook or the ingredients we use can cut down on the calories in any given dish radically. For example, one can have a regular Vegetable Burger which has 433 calories but our low calorie version of the same has only 274 calories. Isn't it amazing how small alterations to a recipe can allow us to enjoy our favourite goodies without harming our health!

The trick here is to let you enjoy all that you wish to eat but to cook in a healthy way. So pack off those excess calories and fat but retain the flavours and taste.

Also included in this book is a comprehensive **calorie counter** which lists the caloric and fat count of all basic ingredients found on every kitchen shelf.

Here's to a lifetime of healthy cooking and eating!

~ CONTENTS ~

High Cal	*Low Cal*

SOUPS & SALAD DRESSINGS

GRAVIES

	High Cal			*Low Cal*	

ALL TIME FAVOURITES

DESSERTS

6

BASIC RECIPES

CALORIE COUNTER

SOUPS & SALAD DRESSINGS

Cream of Tomato Soup

HIGH CAL :	167 cal. per serving ❖ 10.1 gm. fat per serving

Refreshing and creamy, it's sinfully rich with high calorie ingredients like cream and butter. Both these ingredients are rich in saturated fat which gets converted to cholesterol in our body and raises our cholesterol levels. The deep fried bread croutons add more calories to this cream soup. See overleaf, for a healthy version of tomato soup which is devoid of these fatty ingredients and is yet equally delicious.

Preparation time: 10 minutes.   Cooking time: 25 minutes.   Serves 4.

4 cups chopped tomatoes
1 bay leaf (tejpatta)
2 to 3 whole peppercorns
1 tbsp refined flour (maida)
1½ tbsp butter
¼ cup tomato purée

1 to 2 tsp sugar (if required)
1½ tbsp cream
salt and freshly ground pepper to taste

For serving
4 tsp cream
4 tbsp deep fried bread croutons

1. In a pan, combine the tomatoes, bay leaf and peppercorns with 1 cup of water and bring to a boil.
2. Simmer for 10 to 15 minutes till the tomatoes are soft.
3. Remove the bay leaf, cool the mixture and purée it in a blender. Strain the purée and keep aside.
4. Heat the butter in another pan, add the refined flour and cook it over a slow flame for a few seconds.
5. Add 1 cup of water gradually and stir it continuously, so that no lumps remain.
6. Add the puréed tomato mixture, tomato purée, sugar, salt and pepper and bring it to a boil.
7. Add the cream and mix well.
   Serve hot, garnished with a tsp of cream and topped with a tbsp of croutons.

~ **Healthy Tomato Soup** ~

LOW CAL :	97 cal. per serving ◆ 1.4 gm. fat per serving

A *perfect low calorie substitute for creamy tomato soup in which the creamy texture is retained by the addition of protein rich moong dal and low fat milk. The use of only 1 tsp of butter for 4 servings makes this recipe truly healthy. Using toasted whole wheat bread croutons for serving is just the right crunchy contrast to the fried croutons made with oodles of oil and refined flour.*

Preparation time: 5 minutes.   Cooking time: 25 minutes.   Serves 4.

5 cups chopped tomatoes
1/3 cup yellow moong dal (split yellow gram), washed
1/2 cup finely chopped onions
1 tbsp cornflour
1/3 cup warm low fat milk, page 117
1 tsp butter
salt and pepper to taste

For serving
4 tbsp toasted whole wheat bread croutons

1. Pressure cook the tomatoes and the moong dal with 3 to 4 cups of water till the dal is cooked.
2. Cool and blend in a liquidiser. Keep aside.
3. Melt the butter, add the onions, sauté for 3 to 4 minutes and add the puréed mixture.
4. Mix the cornflour with a little water and pour into the soup.
5. Simmer for 2 minutes, stirring occasionally.
6. Add the sugar, milk, salt and pepper and bring to a boil.
   Serve hot each cup garnished with a tbsp of toasted whole wheat bread croutons.

Handy tip: You can replace the butter with 1 tsp of oil in this recipe, since oil has less saturated fat as compared to butter.

Cream of Spinach Soup

HIGH CAL : 106 cal. per serving ❖ 8.6 gm. fat per serving

Spinach, by itself, is a multi-nutrient vegetable and is packed with the goodness of iron, folic acid, vitamin A and vitamin C. Since ages, sumptuous spinach soup has been regarded as best for weight watchers; but only if made without the use of butter and cream.

Preparation time: 5 minutes.   Cooking time: 5 minutes.   Serves 4.

3 cups chopped spinach (palak)
½ cup chopped onions
½ tsp finely chopped garlic
1 tbsp refined flour (maida)
2 tbsp butter
salt and pepper to taste

For the garnish
¼ cup fresh cream

1. Blanch the spinach in boiling water for 10 seconds, remove and immerse in cold water to retain the colour.

2. Drain and purée the spinach in a blender.
3. Heat the butter in a pan and sauté the onions and garlic till the onions turn translucent.
4. Add the flour and sauté till the flour gets a sandy texture.
5. Whisk in 2½ cups of water to the mixture stirring continuously and bring it to a boil till it thickens.
6. Add in the spinach purée and mix well.
7. Season with salt and pepper and bring to a boil.
   Serve hot, garnished with a tbsp of fresh cream in each bowl.

Low Calorie Spinach Soup

| LOW CAL : | 60 cal. per serving ❖ 1.6 gm. fat per serving |

This nourishing spinach soup is low in calories but retains all the essential nutrients. Try your culinary skills in cooking this version of spinach soup and I bet you'll be proud and glad you did it.

Preparation time: 5 minutes.   Cooking time: 5 minutes.   Serves 4.

3 cups chopped spinach (palak)
½ cup chopped onions

½ tsp grated garlic
1½ cups low fat milk, page 117
1 tsp oil
salt and pepper to taste

1. Heat the oil in a pan and sauté the onions and garlic for a few seconds.
2. Add the spinach and salt and sauté for 2 to 3 minutes.
3. Add 1½ cups of water and bring to a boil.
4. Cool and purée in a liquidiser.
5. Add the milk and pepper and bring to a boil again.
   Serve hot.

Thousand Island Dressing

HIGH CAL :	35 cal. per tbsp. ◆ 3.0 gm. fat per tbsp.

An authentic American creamy yoghurt dressing that is mayonnaise based. This vegetarian version enhanced with mustard powder and ketchup combines fresh veggies like capsicum and onion into a sensational blend.

Preparation time: 10 minutes.   No cooking.   Makes 1½ cups (21 tbsp).

1 cup (200 grams) fresh cream
3 tbsp thick curds
3 tbsp tomato ketchup
½ tsp chilli sauce
2 tsp chopped pickled cocktail onions
2 tsp chopped pickled capsicum
¼ tsp chopped green chillies
1 tsp mustard (rai) powder
1 tbsp powdered sugar
salt to taste

1. Whisk the cream until thick.
2. Add the remaining ingredients and mix well.
3. Store refrigerated and use as required.

Handy tips: 1. This dressing should be consumed within 12 hours of making.
2. To make **pickled onions and capsicum**, mix together 1 cup of water, ½ cup vinegar, 2 tsp of sugar and salt to taste and divide into 2 batches. In one, add ¼ cup chopped onions and in the other add ¼ cup of chopped capsicum. Boil both mixtures separately until the vegetables are tender. Cool and store in an air-tight bottle and use as required.

Low Calorie Thousand Island Dressing

LOW CAL :	10 cal. per tbsp. ❖ 0 gm. fat per tbsp.

The art of substitution of ingredients in this exclusive dressing is extremely simple. Though hard to believe, substituting just one ingredient like cream with low fat curds brings down the calories drastically without compromising on the taste. Try this dressing for an afternoon meal to make a sinful salad….. with only one third of the calories.

Preparation time: 10 minutes.   No cooking.   Makes 1½ cups (21 tbsp).

1 cup thick low fat curds, page 118
1 tsp mustard (rai) powder
1 tsp sugar
3 tbsp tomato ketchup
1 tsp chilli sauce
2 tsp chopped pickled cocktail onions
2 tsp chopped pickled capsicum
½ tsp chopped green chilli
salt to taste

1. Whisk the curds thoroughly, ensuring that there are no lumps.

2. Add the remaining ingredients and mix well.
3. Store refrigerated and use as required.

Handy tip : This dressing should be consumed within 12 hours of making it.

～ **Salad Cream** ～

HIGH CAL :	42 cal. per tbsp. ◆ 4.3 gm. fat per tbsp.

A creamy, rich and delicious vegetarian version of mayonnaise that's flavoured with mustard powder and lemon juice. A little difficult to resist, this flavourful dressing is just perfect for underweight people who can afford to put on some extra kilos. Try the Lemony Yoghurt Dressing, page 18, for an equally irresistible low fat dressing.

Preparation time: a few minutes.   No cooking.   Makes ½ cup (7 tbsp).

½ cup (100 gm) fresh cream
2 tbsp salad oil
¼ tsp mustard (rai) powder
1 tsp powdered sugar
1 to 2 tsp lemon juice

¼ tsp pepper
salt to taste

1. Whisk the cream till it is thick.
2. In another bowl, mix all the other ingredients.
3. Combine the cream with the other ingredients. Mix gently so that the cream does not curdle.
4. Store refrigerated and use as required.

～ Lemony Yoghurt Dressing ～

LOW CAL :	3 cal. per tbsp. ◆ 0.1 gm. fat per tbsp.

Creamy low fat curds pair remarkably well with the assertive flavours of basil, pepper, salt and lemon rind. This colourful dressing comes alive, thanks to grated apple and basil. To avoid the usual cholesterol from salad cream, this recipe makes use of low fat curds instead of cream.

Preparation time: 10 minutes.   No cooking.   Makes ½ cup (7 tbsp).

¼ cup low fat curds, page 118
½ tsp grated lemon rind

1 tbsp finely chopped basil
2 tbsp grated apple
salt and pepper to taste

1. Combine all the ingredients in a bowl and mix well.
2. Chill for at least 2 hours. Use as required.

Oil Free Soya Sauce Dressing

LOW CAL : 14 cal. per tbsp. ◆ 0 gm. fat per tbsp.

This piquant dressing adds a touch of China to your menu. Being made only with a blend of herbs and spices, this is absolutely low in calories and so makes an exotic salad if tossed with veggies of your choice and served as a side dish to a main course.

Preparation time: 10 minutes. No cooking. Makes 2 tbsp.

2 cloves garlic
1 to 2 green chillies, chopped
juice of ½ lemon

1 tsp soya sauce
1 tsp sugar

1. Pound the garlic and green chillies in a mortar and pestle.
2. Add the lemon juice, soya sauce and sugar and mix well.
3. Pour into a bottle and keep refrigerated till required.

Oil Free Melon Dressing

LOW CAL : 2 cal. per tbsp. ◆ 0 gm. fat per tbsp.

Let your imagination run wild as you select a sweet fruit like muskmelon and blend it with common flavourings like salt, pepper, coriander and cumin seeds to make this creamy salad dressing that's sure to enliven your meal.

Preparation time: 10 minutes.   No cooking.   Makes 1 cup (14 tbsp).

1 cup chopped ripe muskmelon (kharbooja)
½ tsp roasted cumin seeds (jeera), crushed
3 tbsp chopped coriander
salt and pepper to taste

1. Blend the muskmelon to a smooth purée in a blender.
2. Add the remaining ingredients and mix well. Refrigerate till required.

Handy tip : Select a ripe and flavourful melon for best results.

GRAVIES

Malai Koftas in Makhani Gravy

HIGH CAL : 324 cal. per serving ◆ 27.5 gm. fat per serving

This is a dish I often call for at restaurants. Spicy and soft vegetable dumplings in rich tomato gravy cooked in butter and topped with cream. To suit the purpose of an overweight person who aims to save on calories, all one needs to do is make some minor changes to it as shown in the recipe of Paneer Palak Koftas in Makhani Gravy, page 25. Both are equally tantalizing — I assure you.

Preparation time: 10 minutes.   Cooking time: 30 minutes.   Serves 4.

For the malai koftas
½ cup grated paneer (cottage cheese)
½ cup potatoes, boiled and grated
1 tbsp milk powder
1 tbsp tomato ketchup
1 tsp chilli powder
a pinch turmeric powder (haldi)

¼ cup grated carrots
2 tbsp finely chopped capsicum
1 tsp grated ginger
½ tsp grated garlic
1 tbsp chopped coriander

Other ingredients
oil for deep frying

For the tomato paste
½ cup sliced onions
12 mm. (½") piece ginger, chopped
3 cloves garlic, chopped
2 cups chopped tomatoes
4 to 5 cashewnuts
¼ tsp turmeric powder (haldi)
1 tsp chilli powder

Other ingredients
½ tsp cumin seeds (jeera)
1 tsp garam masala

4 to 5 tbsp cream
½ tsp kasuri methi (dried fenugreek leaves)
2 tsp sugar
4 tbsp butter
salt to taste

For the garnish
1 tbsp chopped coriander
1 tsp butter

For the malai koftas
1. Combine the mixture and divide it into 6 equal parts.
2. Roll them into rounds and deep fry them in oil over a medium flame till they are golden brown. Drain and keep aside.

For the tomato paste
1. Combine the onions, ginger, garlic, tomatoes, cashewnuts, turmeric powder and chilli powder with ½ cup of water in a pan and simmer for 15 to 20 minutes till the vegetables are soft. Cool completely.
2. Blend this mixture in a liquidiser to get a smooth purée.
3. Strain the mixture and keep aside.

How to proceed
1. Heat butter in a and add the cumin seeds. When the seeds crackle, add the prepared tomato paste, garam masala, kasuri methi, sugar and salt and bring to a boil.
2. Add the cream and mix well. Add the koftas and bring to a boil.
   Serve hot, garnished with the chopped coriander and butter.

Paneer Palak Koftas in Makhani Gravy

LOW CAL : 103 cal. per serving ❖ 1.8 gm. fat per serving

This dish is specially prepared for calorie conscious North Indian food fans. Take my word for it - these steamed koftas in a nourishing gravy are finger licking! Serve it with whole wheat parathas to make a satisfying meal.

Preparation time: 15 minutes.   Cooking time: 25 minutes.   Serves 4.

For the paneer palak koftas
½ cup spinach (palak), blanched, drained and chopped
½ cup grated low fat paneer (cottage cheese), page 118
3 tsp rice flour (chawal ka atta)
½ green chilli, finely chopped

25

salt to taste

For the makhani gravy
3 cups chopped tomatoes
½ cup chopped onions
2 large cloves garlic, chopped
12 mm. (½") piece ginger, chopped
2 cloves (laung)
25 mm. (1") piece cinnamon (dalchini)
¼ cup chopped red pumpkin (kaddu)
½ tsp cumin seeds (jeera)
¼ tsp kasuri methi (dried fenugreek leaves)
1 tsp chilli powder
½ cup low fat milk, page 117
½ tsp cornflour
½ tsp sugar
1 tsp oil
salt to taste

For the garnish
1 tbsp chopped coriander

For the paneer palak koftas
1. Combine all the ingredients in a bowl and mix well.
2. Divide the mixture into 12 equal portions. Shape each portion into an even sized round.
3. Steam the koftas for 4 to 5 minutes. Keep aside till required.

For the makhani gravy
1. Combine the tomatoes, onions, garlic, ginger, cloves, cinnamon and red pumpkin with ¾ cup of water and cook over a slow flame till the vegetables are soft. Allow the mixture to cool completely. Remove the cinnamon and cloves and discard them.
2. Blend the tomato mixture to a smooth purée.
3. Heat the oil in a non-stick pan and add the cumin seeds.
4. When the seeds crackle, add the kasuri methi and chilli powder and sauté for a few seconds. Add 1 tbsp of water if the chilli powder begins to burn.
5. Add the puréed tomato mixture, sugar and salt and bring to a boil.
6. Dissolve the cornflour in the milk and add it to the prepared gravy. Simmer for a few minutes till the gravy thickens.

How to proceed

1. Just before serving, reheat the gravy, slide the koftas into the gravy and bring to a boil.
2. Serve hot, garnished with the chopped coriander.

Handy tips:
  1. Adjust the consistency of the gravy by adding water if necessary before serving.
  2. 2½ cups chopped spinach gives you ½ cup of blanched and chopped spinach.
  3. Squeeze out all the water from the blanched spinach to make koftas.

Methi Malai Mutter

| HIGH CAL : | 227 cal. per serving ❖ 15.6 gm. fat per serving |

This popular Punjabi dish is made with vitamin A and iron rich fenugreek and fibre laden green peas. But not all dishes made with these two versatile ingredients are nutritious and healthy. Paneer (whole fat milk), oil, butter, cream and cashewnuts in all constitute approximately 165 calories out of the total of 227 calories per serving which can be avoided if you take a look at the low calorie version, page 31.

Preparation time: 15 minutes.   Cooking time: 25 minutes.   Serves 4.

1½ cups chopped fenugreek (methi) leaves
¾ cup green peas, boiled
1 cup grated paneer (cottage cheese)
1 bay leaf (tejpatta)
25 mm. (1") piece cinnamon (dalchini)
2 cloves (laung)
2 cardamoms (elaichi)
½ tsp chopped garlic
½ tsp grated ginger
¼ cup chopped tomatoes
¼ cup spinach (palak) purée
½ tsp garam masala
½ tsp sugar
2 tbsp milk
2 tbsp cream
2 tsp butter
2 tsp oil
salt to taste

For the white gravy
½ cup sliced onions

5 cashewnuts
1 tbsp charmagaz
25 mm. (1") piece cinnamon (dalchini)
2 cloves (laung)
2 green chillies

For the white gravy
1. Combine all the ingredients with ¾ cup of water and simmer for about 15 minutes.
2. Remove and discard the cloves and cinnamon.
3. Cool and blend to a smooth paste. Keep aside.

How to proceed
1. Add the methi leaves to boiling water and simmer for about 2 to 3 minutes.
2. Drain out the water and keep the methi aside.
3. Heat the butter and oil in a pan and add the bay leaf, cinnamon, cloves and cardamoms to it. Add the methi leaves and sauté for 2 to 3 minutes.
4. Add the garlic and ginger and sauté for 2 minutes.
5. Add the tomatoes and sauté for 2 to 3 minutes.
6. Add the white gravy, spinach purée, garam masala, sugar, milk, cream, green peas, paneer and salt and cook till the gravy thickens.
   Serve hot.

Handy tip : To make spinach purée, clean the spinach leaves, blanch them in hot water, drain and grind. About 1 cup spinach leaves give ¼ cup of purée.

Methi Mutter Pasanda

LOW CAL :	86 cal. per serving ◆ 1.4 gm. fat per serving

This recipe brings down the calories of this subzi from 227 to 86 per serving. While aiming to lose weight healthily, rely on flavour intense herbs instead of fat laden ingredients to maximize the taste and minimize the fat and calories as I've done in this recipe. After you get a hang of it, experiment each dish with your own combinations. You will definitely be pleased to experience a variety of flavours in your cooking....... that are delicious and low in calories.

Preparation time: 15 minutes.   Cooking time: 30 minutes.   Serves 4.

1 cup green peas, boiled
1 cup finely chopped fenugreek (methi) leaves
¼ tsp cumin seeds (jeera)
½ tsp kasuri methi (dried fenugreek leaves)

¼ cup low fat milk, page 117
¼ cup low fat curds, page 118
½ tsp Bengal gram flour (besan)
¼ tsp garam masala
1 tsp oil
salt to taste

For the paste
1¼ cups sliced onions
¼ cup finely chopped cauliflower
1 to 2 green chillies, chopped
2 large cloves garlic, chopped
12 mm. (½") piece ginger, sliced
25 mm (1") piece cinnamon (dalchini)
1 clove (laung)
1 cup low fat milk, page 117

For the paste
1. Combine all the ingredients in a pan and simmer for 8 to 10 minutes till the onions are soft and nearly all the liquid has evaporated. Remove and discard the clove and cinnamon. Cool completely.

2. Purée the mixture to a smooth paste in a blender. Keep aside.

How to proceed
1. Combine the milk, curds and gram flour in a bowl. Mix well and keep aside.
2. Sprinkle salt over the fenugreek leaves and leave aside for 10 minutes. Drain out the liquid and squeeze out all the water.
3. Heat the oil in a non-stick pan and add the cumin seeds.
4. When the seeds crackle, add the fenugreek leaves and kasuri methi and sauté for 3 to 4 minutes.
5. Add the prepared paste, curd-gram flour mixture, garam masala and salt with ½ cup of water and bring it to a boil.
6. Add the green peas and simmer for 1 to 2 minutes.
   Serve hot.

Pakoda Kadhi

HIGH CAL : 155 cal. per serving ❖ 11.2 gm. fat per serving

This is the traditional way that pakoda kadhi is made. Deep-fried spinach pakodas simmered in a yoghurt gravy. Research shows that cutting down fat from our diet instead of the amount we eat is a healthy way to lose weight while fulfilling all our nutrient needs. So Steamed Pakoda Kadhi, page 36, is a specially modified recipe towards this direction.

Preparation time: 15 minutes.   Cooking time: 20 minutes.   Serves 4.

For the palak pakodas
1 cup spinach (palak), blanched, drained and chopped
¼ cup Bengal gram flour (besan)
½ tsp chilli powder
½ tsp cumin seeds (jeera)
a pinch soda bi-carbonate
salt to taste
oil for deep frying

For the kadhi

1 cup curds
2 tbsp Bengal gram flour (besan)
1 tsp cumin seeds (jeera)
a pinch asafoetida (hing)
5 curry leaves
½ cup sliced onions
2 cloves garlic, finely chopped
¼ tsp turmeric powder (haldi)
1 tbsp oil
salt to taste

For the palak pakodas

1. Mix the spinach, gram flour, chilli powder, cumin seeds, soda bi-carb and salt with enough water in a bowl to make a soft dough.
2. Mix well, divide into 8 equal portions and shape into even-sized rounds.
3. Heat the oil in a kadai and deep fry the pakodas over a medium flame till they are golden brown.
4. Remove and drain on absorbent paper. Keep aside.

For the kadhi
1. Mix the curds and gram flour in a bowl. Keep aside.
2. Heat the oil in a pan and add the cumin seeds. When they crackle, add the asafoetida, curry leaves, onions and garlic and sauté for 4 to 5 minutes.
3. Add the curds and gram flour mixture, turmeric powder, salt and 1 cup of water and bring to a boil, stirring continuously.

How to proceed
Add the palak pakodas to the hot kadhi and simmer for 4 to 5 minutes, just before serving. Serve hot with rice.

～ Steamed Pakoda Kadhi ～

LOW CAL :	86 cal. per serving ❖ 1.7 gm. fat per serving

The radish pakodas in this recipe are steamed in the kadhi and not deep fried. You can also replace the radish with spinach if you like. This simple combination of radish and low fat curds needs only steamed rice to complete your meal. It is also a good way to add vegetables to your diet to provide vitamin A and iron. The curd and besan combination makes the kadhi a rich source of protein and calcium too.

Preparation time: 15 minutes.   Cooking time: 30 minutes.   Serves 4.

For the steamed pakodas
¼ cup yellow moong dal (split yellow gram), soaked
¼ cup grated radish (mooli)
½ tsp ginger-green chilli paste
1 to 2 tbsp Bengal gram flour (besan)
salt to taste

For the kadhi
1 cup low fat curds, page 118
2 tbsp Bengal gram flour (besan)
1 tsp cumin seeds (jeera)
¼ tsp asafoetida (hing)
1 tsp ginger-green chilli paste
a pinch turmeric powder (haldi)
1 tsp oil
salt to taste

For the garnish
2 tbsp chopped coriander

For the steamed pakodas
1. Drain out all the water from the dal and grind in a blender to a coarse paste, without using water.
2. Squeeze all the liquid out of the grated radish and add the radish to the ground moong dal (add the liquid to the curds mixture).
3. Add the ginger-green chilli paste, gram flour and salt and mix well. Keep aside.

For the kadhi
1. Whisk the curds along with the gram flour till the mixture is smooth and no lumps remain. Add the ginger- green chilli paste and turmeric powder and mix well.
2. Heat the oil in a non-stick pan and add the cumin seeds. When they crackle, add the asafoetida.
3. Add the curds mixture, salt, 2½ cups of water and continue stirring till it comes to a boil.
4. Drop teaspoonfuls of the pakoda mixture into the boiling kadhi and allow it to boil till the pakodas are cooked (approx. 5 to 7 minutes).
   Serve hot, garnished with the chopped coriander.

Handy tip: When you add the pakodas into the kadhi, add one first and check again to see that it does not crumble or disintegrate. If that happens, add some more gram flour to the pakoda mixture and check.

~ Nawabi Curry ~

HIGH CAL : 85 cal. per serving ◆ 6.6 gm. fat per serving

A rich Moghlai style curry which is traditionally made creamier by the addition of cashewnuts, almonds, coconut and khus-khus. You will be surprised to know that avoiding these high calorie ingredients, to make a low cal version, makes an equally mouth-watering Nawabi Curry. Try the Low Calorie Nawabi Curry, page 41.

Preparation time: 15 minutes.   Cooking time: 20 minutes.   Serves 4.

1½ cups chopped tomatoes
1 cup chopped mixed boiled vegetables
a few strands of saffron (optional)
1 tsp sugar
4 tbsp ghee
salt to taste

To be ground into a paste (for the curry)
1 cup sliced onions
1 tbsp cashewnuts
1 tbsp almonds (optional)

1 tbsp coriander (dhania) seeds
1 tbsp cumin seeds (jeera)
1 tbsp khus-khus (poppy seeds)
2 tsp aniseeds (saunf)
2 tbsp grated fresh coconut
25 mm. (1") piece ginger
2 green chillies
4 red chillies
1 to 2 cardamoms (elaichi)
2 cloves (laung)
25 mm. (1") piece cinnamon (dalchini)
7 curry leaves

1. Add 1½ cups of water to the tomatoes and boil for 10 to 12 minutes. When soft, cool and prepare a purée by straining the mixture through a sieve.
2. Heat the ghee in a pan and sauté the ground paste for 4 to 5 minutes. Add the tomato purée, sugar and salt.
3. Warm the saffron in a small vessel, add a little milk, rub in until the saffron dissolves and add to the curry.
4. Add the boiled vegetables and bring to a boil.
   Serve hot.

Low Calorie Nawabi Curry

LOW CAL : 34 cal. per serving ◆ 1.0 gm. fat per serving

Discover a new way to make a creamy, flavourful and low calorie gravy. Packed with delicate seasonings and spices, this makes a wonderful fare especially when served hot with phulkas. Apart from being a low calorie recipe, this curry has a wealth of nutrients like vitamins A and C.

Preparation time: 30 minutes.   Cooking time: 20 minutes.   Serves 4.

1½ cups chopped tomatoes
1 cup chopped mixed boiled vegetables
½ tsp sugar
1 tsp oil
salt to taste

To be ground into a paste (for the curry)
1 cup sliced onions
1 tbsp coriander (dhania) seeds
1 tbsp cumin seeds (jeera)
1 tbsp khus-khus (poppy seeds)
2 tsp aniseeds (saunf)

25 mm. (1") piece ginger
2 green chillies
3 cardamoms (elaichi)
2 cloves (laung)
25 mm. (1") piece cinnamon (dalchini)

1. Add 1 cup of water to the tomatoes and cook until soft. Cool completely.
2. Pass through a blender to make a tomato purée.
3. Heat the oil in a pan and sauté the ground paste for 2 to 3 minutes.
4. Add the tomato purée, vegetables, sugar and salt and simmer for 5 to 7 minutes. Serve hot.

Dal Makhani

HIGH CAL : 236 cal. per serving ❖ 10.0 gm. fat per serving

Dal Makhani is a robust preparation - a celebrated delicacy from Punjab. Whole urad and rajma are cooked in an onion-tomato gravy, perked with spices and garnished with butter which adds unnecessary cholesterol to our diet. Turn over, for a flavourful and healthier version of this dal!

Preparation time: 15 minutes.   Cooking time: 20 to 25 minutes.   Serves 4.

¾ cup whole urad (whole black lentils)
2 tbsp rajma (kidney beans)
1 tsp cumin seeds (jeera)
2 green chilles, slit
25 mm. (1") piece cinnamon (dalchini)
2 cloves (laung)
3 cardamoms (elaichi)
½ cup finely chopped onions
½ tsp ginger-garlic paste
1 tsp chilli powder
¼ tsp turmeric powder (haldi)
1½ cups fresh tomato pulp
¾ cup (150 gms) cream
3 tbsp butter
salt to taste

For the garnish
2 tbsp chopped coriander
1 tbsp butter

1. Clean, wash and soak the whole urad and rajma overnight. Drain and keep aside.

2. Combine the dals and salt with 2 cups of water and pressure cook till the dal is overcooked. Whisk well till the dal is almost mashed.
3. Heat the butter in a pan and add the cumin seeds.
4. When the cumin seeds crackle, add the green chillies, cinnamon, cloves, cardamoms, onions and ginger-garlic paste and sauté till the onions turn golden brown in colour.
5. Add the chilli powder, turmeric powder and tomato pulp and cook over a medium flame till the oil separates from the tomato gravy.
6. Add the dal mixture, ¾ cup of water and salt if required and simmer for 10 to 15 minutes.
7. Add the cream and mix well.
8. Garnish with the chopped coriander and butter and serve hot.

Handy tip : You will require 4 medium tomatoes to make 1½ cups fresh tomato pulp.

Low Calorie Dal Makhani

LOW CAL : 134 cal. per serving ❖ 1.7 gm. fat per serving

*H*ere's an old favourite served in a new-fangled, but yet healthy way. Being cooked only in 1 tsp of oil, this dal is a perfect accompaniment to whole wheat parathas for weight watchers. Serve hot, to relish the flavours.

Preparation time: 15 minutes.   Cooking time: 20 to 25 minutes.   Serves 4.

½ cup whole urad (whole black lentils)
1 tbsp rajma (kidney beans)
1 cup low fat milk, page 117
½ tsp cumin seeds (jeera)
½ cup finely chopped onions
1 tsp ginger-garlic paste
1 tsp chilli powder
¼ tsp turmeric powder (haldi)
2 tsp coriander (dhania) powder
¾ cup fresh tomato pulp
1 tsp oil
salt to taste

For the garnish
2 tbsp chopped coriander

1. Clean, wash and soak the whole urad and rajma overnight. Drain and keep aside.
2. Combine the dals and salt with 2 cups of water and pressure cook till the dal is overcooked. Whisk well till the dal is almost mashed.
3. Add the milk and 1 cup of water and simmer for 10 minutes while stirring occasionally.
4. Heat the oil in a non-stick pan and add the cumin seeds.
5. When the seeds crackle, add the onions and ginger- garlic paste and sauté till the onion, turn golden brown in colour.
6. Add the chilli powder, turmeric powder, coriander powder and tomato pulp with ¼ cup of water and sauté for 5 to 7 minutes.
7. Add this to the dal mixture and simmer for 10 to 12 minutes till the dal is thick and creamy.
   Serve hot, garnished with the chopped coriander.

ALL TIME FAVOURITES

Pizza Margherita

| HIGH CAL : | 273 cal. per serving ❖ 15.2 gm. fat per serving |

Pizza is everyone's favourite fast food. A soft crust topped with a zesty tomato sauce and smothered with a generous layer of cheese. Difficult to resist? To make it a part of your healthy diet, all you need to do is to trim off all the excessive visible and invisible fat to make a low fat version viz. Dieter's Pizza, page 51

Preparation time: 10 minutes.   Cooking time: 40 minutes.
Makes 2 pizzas (8 servings).   Baking time: 25 minutes.
Baking temperature: 200°C (400°F).

For the pizza base
2 cups refined flour (maida)
2 tsp (10 grams) crumbled fresh yeast
1 tsp sugar
1 tbsp olive oil or oil

For the pizza sauce
4 large tomatoes
2 bay leaves (tejpatta)
4 to 6 peppercorns
½ cup chopped onions
1 tsp chopped garlic
¼ cup chopped capsicum
2 tbsp tomato purée (optional)
¼ cup tomato ketchup
1 tsp sugar (optional)
½ tsp dried oregano
2 tbsp olive oil or oil
salt to taste

Other ingredients
10 to 12 roughly chopped fresh basil leaves
1 cup grated cooking cheese or mozzarella cheese
2 tbsp olive oil
butter or oil for greasing

For the pizza base

1. Combine all the ingredients except the oil in a bowl and knead into a soft dough using enough water until it is smooth and elastic (approx. 5 to 7 minutes).
2. Add the oil and knead again.
3. Cover the dough with a wet muslin cloth and allow it to prove till it doubles in volume (approx. 15 to 20 minutes).
4. Press the dough lightly to remove the air.
5. Divide the dough into 2 equal parts.
6. Roll each portion into a circle of 250 mm. (10") diameter and 6 mm. (¼") thickness.

For the pizza sauce

1. Blanch the tomatoes in boiling water.
2. Peel, cut into quarters and deseed the tomatoes.
3. Chop them finely and keep the tomato pulp aside.
4. Heat the oil, add the bay leaves and peppercorns and sauté for a few seconds.
5. Add the onions, garlic and capsicum and sauté for a few minutes.
6. Add the chopped tomatoes and allow it to simmer for 10 to 15 minutes until the sauce reduces a little.
7. Add the tomato purée, ketchup, sugar and salt and simmer for some more time.
8. Finally, add the oregano and mix well. Remove the bay leaves and peppercorns and discard.

How to proceed

1. Place one pizza base on a greased baking tray.
2. Spread half the pizza sauce on the pizza base.
3. Sprinkle with half the basil leaves and cheese on top of the pizza.
4. Drizzle with half of the oil and bake in a pre-heated oven at 200°C (400°F) for 20 minutes or until the base is evenly browned.
5. Repeat with the remaining ingredients to make another pizza.
   Serve hot.

Variation : SKILLET MARGHERITA

Cook the pizza in a non-stick pan instead of baking it in the oven. Cover the pan with a lid and cook on a very slow flame for 10 to 12 minutes or till the base is golden brown and the cheese has melted.

~ Dieter's Pizza ~

LOW CAL : 140 cal. per serving ◆ 1.8 gm. fat per serving

Low fat paneer, tomato sauce and nourishing vegetables have turned a calorie-laden pizza to a humble dieter's pizza with equally tempting flavours.

Preparation time: 30 minutes. Cooking time: 45 minutes.
Makes 2 pizzas (8 servings). Baking time: 20 minutes.
Baking temperature: 200°C (400°F).

For the pizza base
2 cups whole wheat flour (gehun ka atta)
2 tsp (10 grams) crumbled fresh yeast
a pinch sugar
1 tsp salt

For the tomato sauce
4 large tomatoes
½ cup chopped onions
3 to 4 peppercorns
1 bay leaf (tejpatta)

51

¼ cup finely chopped capsicum
1 tsp chopped garlic
½ tsp dried oregano
1 tsp oil
salt to taste

For the cheesy topping
½ recipe low fat cream cheese, page 121
2 tbsp low fat milk, page 117
½ tsp prepared mustard

Other ingredients
½ cup sliced zucchini (optional)
½ cup sliced onions
1 tomato, sliced
10 to 12 basil leaves
1 tsp oil for greasing

For the pizza base
1. Combine all the ingredients in a bowl. Knead into a soft dough using enough
   water until it is smooth and elastic.

2. Cover the dough with a wet muslin cloth and allow it to prove till it doubles in volume (approx. 15 to 20 minutes).
3. Press the dough lightly to remove the air.
4. Divide the dough into 2 equal parts.
5. Roll out each portion into a circle of 250 mm. (10") diameter and 6 mm. (¼") thickness.

For the tomato sauce
1. Blanch the tomatoes in boiling water.
2. Peel, cut into quarters and deseed the tomatoes. Chop finely and keep the tomatoes aside.
3. Heat the oil and add the peppercorns and bay leaf and sauté for a few seconds.
4. Add the onions, capsicum and garlic and sauté for a few seconds.
5. Add the chopped tomato pulp and allow it to simmer for 10 to 15 minutes until the sauce reduces a little.
6. Add salt and simmer for some more time.
7. Finally, add the oregano and mix well. Remove and discard the bay leaf and peppercorns. Keep aside.

For the cheesy topping

Blend the cream cheese, milk and prepared mustard to a thick purée in a liquidiser and keep aside.

How to proceed

1. Place one pizza base on a lightly greased baking tray.
2. Spread half the tomato sauce over the pizza base and top with half the cheesy topping mixture.
3. Arrange half the zucchini, onions and tomato slices on the pizza and top with some basil leaves.
4. Bake in a pre-heated oven at 200°C (400°F) for 10 to 15 minutes or till the base is evenly browned. Top with some more basil leaves.
5. Make another pizza using the other pizza base and the remaining ingredients. Serve hot.

Handy tip: Prepared mustard is a proprietory product available at most provision stores. It's a yellow coloured paste that has a sharp vinegar-like taste and is also called French style mustard.

~ Vegetable Burger ~

Picture on cover.

HIGH CAL :	433 cal. per burger ◆ 21.8 gm. fat per burger

An all time favourite snack, adored by kids and elders which is always looked at suspiciously due to the abundance of calories (433 per burger). But now you need not give up your favourite snack. Instead make it suit your purpose by minimizing the fat and calories coming from fatty ingredients like cream, mayonnaise and cheese as I've done in the recipe of Whole Wheat Vegetable Burger, page 58.

Preparation time: 15 minutes.   Cooking time: 20 minutes.   Makes 6 burgers.

For the burgers
6 burger buns

For the vegetable cutlets
1½ cups chopped mixed boiled vegetables
1 cup potatoes, boiled and mashed
1 slice bread
½ tsp chilli-ginger paste
1 tsp lemon juice

1 tsp garam masala
salt to taste
1 cup bread crumbs
oil for deep frying

To be mixed into coleslaw
1 cup shredded cabbage
½ cup grated carrot
1 recipe salad cream, page 17

For the filling
½ recipe salad cream, page 17
3 tbsp tomato ketchup
12 lettuce leaves
6 onion slices
12 cucumber slices
12 tomato slices
6 slices cheese

For the vegetable cutlets
1. Dip the bread slice in water for a few seconds. Squeeze out the water and crumble

the bread.

2. Mix the vegetables, potatoes, crumbled bread, chilli-ginger paste, lemon juice, garam masala and salt and divide the mixture into 6 equal portions.
3. Shape into small flattened rounds and coat with bread crumbs. Press them firmly so that they stick to the surface.
4. Deep fry in hot oil till the cutlets are golden brown.

How to serve
1. Cut each bun horizontally into two and toast them lightly in an oven or on a tava (griddle).
2. Spread a little tomato ketchup and salad cream on the lower half.
3. Place 2 lettuce leaves on each bun and top with some coleslaw.
4. Place a cutlet on top and then 1 onion slice, 2 cucumber slices, 2 tomato slices and 1 cheese slice.
5. Spread some salad cream on top and then cover with the remaining half of the bun.
6. Repeat with the remaining ingredients to make 5 more burgers.

~ Whole Wheat Vegetable Burger ~

LOW CAL : | 274 cal. per burger ◆ 3.2 gm. fat per burger

A perfect healthy fast food for lunch or a snack. Spicy cutlets made with nourishing bulgur wheat and vegetables and stuffed between whole wheat buns add more value to a low fat lunch already packed with nutrients like protein, calcium, iron and vitamin A.

Preparation time: 15 minutes.   Cooking time: 5 minutes.   Makes 6 burgers.

For the burger
6 brown bread buns

For the cutlets
½ cup broken wheat (dalia)
¾ cup grated carrot
½ cup finely chopped onions
¾ cup finely chopped mushrooms
½ cup grated low fat paneer (cottage cheese), page 118
1 tbsp soya sauce
1 tbsp chilli sauce

2 tbsp whole wheat flour (gehun ka atta)
salt and pepper to taste
1½ tsp oil for cooking

For the filling
12 lettuce leaves
6 onion slices
12 cucumber slices
12 tomato slices
2 tsp tomato ketchup mixed with 1 tsp chilli sauce (optional)
½ recipe low calorie thousand island dressing, page 16
mustard sauce to taste

For the cutlets
1. Clean and wash the broken wheat thoroughly. Soak it in 1 cup of hot water for 15 minutes. Drain out the water and discard.
2. Combine all the ingredients in a bowl and mix well.
3. Divide the mixture into 6 equal parts and shape into patties.
4. Cook on a non-stick pan using a little oil till both the sides are golden brown.

How to proceed

1. Slice each bun into two and toast lightly in an oven or on a tava (griddle).
2. On each cut portion of the buns, apply a little mustard sauce and a little tomato ketchup.
3. Spread some of the low calorie thousand island dressing on top.
4. Arrange 2 lettuce leaves, then 1cutlet, 1 onion slice, 2 cucumber slices and 2 tomato slices and cover with the remaining part of the bun.
   Serve immediately.

Bhel Puri

HIGH CAL :	412 cal. per serving ❖ 17.3 gm. fat per serving

Bhel puri is sold in every street corner of Mumbai. You will be surprised to know that this delicious feast contributes 337 calories per serving from sev, papadis and chutneys out of the total of 412 calories per serving. So why not try a new version of Bhel with a good combination of sprouts and fruits providing you with vitamins, fibre and only 163 calories per serving. Refer to page 62, for this excellent snack.

Preparation time: 10 minutes.   No cooking.   Serves 4.

4 cups puffed rice (mumara)
1 cup sev or nylon sev
20 papadis (puris)
½ cup chopped onions
½ cup boiled and chopped potatoes
2 tsp fresh garlic chutney
8 tbsp khajur imli ki chutney
4 tbsp green chutney
1 tsp black salt (sanchal)
juice of lemon
salt to taste

For the garnish
8 papadis (puris), crushed
1 tbsp finely chopped raw mango (optional)
4 tbsp sev or nylon sev
2 tbsp chopped coriander

1. Combine all the ingredients in a large bowl and toss gently till all the ingredients are mixed well.
2. Divide into 4 equal portions and garnish each portion with the papadis, raw

mango, sev and coriander.
Serve immediately.

Sprout and Fruit Bhel

LOW CAL : 163 cal. per serving ◆ 3.8 gm. fat per serving

Here's a healthy alternative to regular calorie-laden bhel. I've added sprouts to this bhel as they are easier to digest and also abound in nutrients like protein, calcium, iron and vitamin C. Mixed with fruits like apple, orange and pomegranate and flavoured with lemon juice, it makes a tantalizingly chatpata snack that's sure to lift your spirits.

Preparation time: 10 minutes.   Cooking time: 10 minutes.   Serves 4.

For the sev-mumara
2 cups puffed rice (mumara)
½ cup sev or nylon sev
½ tsp cumin seeds (jeera)
a pinch asafoetida (hing)
¼ tsp turmeric powder (haldi)

¼ tsp black salt (sanchal)
½ tsp oil

Other ingredients
⅓ cup moong sprouts
⅓ cup chopped tomatoes
⅓ cup chopped apple
2 tbsp chopped raw mango
¼ cup fresh pomegranate seeds
½ cup orange segments
4 tbsp chopped coriander
4 tsp lemon juice
salt to taste

For the sev-mumara
1. Heat the oil in a pan and add the cumin seeds. When they crackle, add the asafoetida, turmeric powder and puffed rice and mix well.
2. Add the black salt and sev. Mix well and cool completely.
3. Store in an air-tight container and use as required.

How to proceed
Mix all the ingredients together and serve immediately.

Masala French Fries

HIGH CAL : 163 cal. per serving ✦ 10.1 gm. fat per serving

An all-time favourite dish relished by all of us, inspite of the fact that it is full of calories. However it is not the potato, but the oil used for frying, which substantially increases the calories and makes it almost double. Try the recipe of Low Fat Fries, on facing page, to discover that you can eat as many as you want without any guilt.

Preparation time: 10 minutes.   Cooking time: 15 minutes.   Serves 2.

2 large potatoes, peeled and cut into fingers
½ tsp chilli powder
½ tsp cumin (jeera) powder
¼ tsp black salt (sanchal)
salt to taste

Other ingredients
oil for deep frying
lemon wedges to serve

1. Parboil the potatoes in salted water for 5 to 7 minutes.
2. Drain and keep aside.
3. Mix the chilli powder, cumin powder, black salt and salt in a small bowl and keep aside.
4. Deep fry the potato fingers in hot oil over a medium flame till they are crisp.
5. Drain on absorbent paper and sprinkle the masala mixture on top.
   Serve hot, with lemon wedges and ketchup.

Handy tip: For really crisp French fries, use a variety of potatoes with a higher starch content popularly known as French Fries Potatoes / chip potatoes. In Maharashtra, they are called Talegaon potatoes.

Low Fat Fries

LOW CAL : 95 cal. per serving ◆ 2.6 gm. fat per serving

Here's a healthy way of making fries using just a tsp of oil instead of deep frying them in oil. This helps you to savour the taste of French fries without adding unnecessary inches to your waist.

Preparation time: 15 minutes.   Cooking time: 20 minutes.   Serves 2.

2 large potatoes, peeled and cut into fingers
1 tsp chilli powder
½ tsp roasted cumin (jeera) powder
1 tsp oil
salt to taste

1. Parboil the potatoes in salted water for 5 to 7 minutes.
2. Drain and keep aside.
3. Mix the chilli powder, cumin powder and salt in a bowl, sprinkle over the potato fingers and coat them well.
4. Heat the oil in a broad non-stick pan and add the potatoes.
5. Cook them over a slow flame till they are crisp and browned on all sides turning them carefully with a fork.
   Serve hot.

Dahi Vada

HIGH CAL : 206 cal. per vada ❖ 10.2 gm. fat per vada

Dahi Bhalla or Dahi Vada? By whatever name you call it, this dish is as popular in the North as in the West. In the North of India, it is served without the khajur imli ki chutney while in the western parts of India, this dish has the added sweet and sour flavours of Khajur Imli ki Chutney and is called Dahi Vada.

Preparation time: 20 minutes.   Cooking time: 15 minutes.   Makes 8 dahi vadas.

For the vadas
1 cup urad dal (split black lentils)
12 mm. (½") piece ginger
2 green chillies
a pinch soda bi-carb
salt to taste
oil for deep frying

For serving
3 cups curds, whisked
2 tbsp khajur imli ki chutney
salt to taste

For the garnish
chilli powder
roasted cumin (jeera) powder

For the vadas
1. Soak the urad dal in water for 3 to 4 hours.
2. Wash and drain the urad dal.
3. Combine the urad dal, ginger and green chillies and grind to a smooth paste in a blender.
4. Add the soda bi-carb and salt to the urad dal paste and mix well till the batter is light and fluffy. Add a little water if required.
5. Wet your hands and take 2 tbsp of the batter on your palm or on a sheet of wet plastic and shape into a circle of 75 mm. (3") diameter. Deep fry in hot oil on a slow flame till the vadas are golden brown, for about 10 minutes. Drain on absorbent paper and keep aside.

How to proceed
1. Soak the deep fried vadas in warm water for about 45 minutes.
2. Just before serving, drain and squeeze out the excess water.
3. Arrange the vadas on a serving dish and top with the whisked curds.
4. Garnish with the chilli powder, cumin powder and salt and serve with khajur imli ki chutney.

~ **Non-Fried Dahi Vada** ~

LOW CAL :	103 cal. per vada ◆ 0.9 gm. fat per vada

Here's a healthy variation of fried dahi vada made using a sandwich toaster. For a guilt free snack, top them with spicy tempered low fat curds and go ahead and eat as much as you can.

Preparation time: 15 minutes.   Cooking time: 15 minutes.   Makes 8 vadas.

For the vadas
1 cup green moong dal (split green gram)
2 green chillies
a pinch asafoetida (hing)
1 tsp fruit salt

For the curds
3 cups low fat curds, page 118
½ tsp mustard seeds (rai)
3 green chillies, broken into pieces
a pinch asafoetida (hing)
1 tsp oil

For the garnish
2 pinches cumin (jeera) powder
2 pinches chilli powder
1 tbsp chopped coriander (optional)
salt to taste

For the vadas
1. Clean, wash and soak the moong dal for 3 to 4 hours.
2. Drain and keep aside.
3. Add the green chillies and blend in a mixer with very little water to make a thick batter.
4. Add the asafoetida and fruit salt and mix well.
5. Heat a non-stick sandwhich toaster and spread some of the mixture in each cavity. Close and heat. When ready, the mixture will be toasted into triangular shaped pieces.
6. Remove the toasted pieces and soak them in water for 20 minutes. Thereafter, squeeze out the water and arrange the vadas on a plate.

For the curds
1. Whisk the curds with salt and refrigerate till required.

2. Heat the oil in a pan and add the mustard seeds.
3. When the seeds crackle, add the asafoetida and green chillies. Add this to the whisked curds and mix well.

How to proceed
Spread the seasoned curds over the vadas. Sprinkle the cumin powder, chilli powder and coriander on top and serve. If you like, also add the khajur imli ki chutney.

Handy tip : Add the fruit salt just before you are ready to cook the dahi vadas.

Sev Puri

HIGH CAL :	318 cal. per serving ❖ 13.9 gm. fat per serving

Sev puri, as the name says is sev topped on papadis along with potatoes and chutneys. Tangy, crisp and tongue-tickling are the words that come to my mind when I think of this chat-pata snack. But we all often tend to avoid this because of its high caloric value. I have specially modified this recipe for food lovers who wish to enjoy their meals while planning a weight loss programme. Check page 73, for such a modified version.

Preparation time: 10 minutes.   No cooking.   Serves 4.

24 papadis (puris)
½ cup boiled and chopped potatoes
½ cup finely chopped onions
2 tbsp finely chopped raw mango
2 tsp fresh garlic chutney
8 tbsp khajur imli ki chutney
4 tbsp green chutney
1 tsp chaat masala
juice of 1 lemon
salt to taste

For the garnish
½ cup sev or nylon sev
2 tbsp chopped coriander

1. Arrange the papadis on a serving plate.
2. Top each papadi with a little potatoes, onions and raw mango.
3. Spoon some fresh garlic chutney, khajur imli ki chutney and green chutney.

4. Sprinkle the chaat masala, lemon juice and salt on top.
5. Garnish with the sev and coriander.
   Serve immediately.

Corn Sev Puri

LOW CAL : 189 cal. per serving ♦ 6.0 gm. fat per serving

Our regular version of this Indian snack has been lightened up by the use of baked puris topped with spicy corn topping and nourishing tamatar ki chutney. So here's to saving calories and helping you enjoy your fare. Make a whole recipe of the papadis and chutney and store for when you are hungry.

Preparation time: 5 minutes.   Cooking time: 20 minutes.   Serves 4.
Baking time: 15 minutes.   Baking temperature: 200°C (400°F).

For the baked papadis
½ cup whole wheat flour (gehun ka atta)
1 tsp oil

¼ tsp salt

To be mixed together into a corn topping
1 cup yellow corn kernels, boiled
1 cup chopped spring onions
2 green chillies, finely chopped
½ cup finely chopped tomatoes
1 tsp chaat masala
2 tsp lemon juice
salt to taste

For the tamatar ki chutney
2 medium sized tomatoes
¼ tsp ajwain (carom seeds)
a pinch asafoetida (hing)
½ tsp grated garlic
½ tsp chilli powder
1 tsp sugar
1 tsp oil
salt to taste

Other ingredients
1 cup sev or nylon sev
¼ cup fresh pomegranate (anar)
2 tbsp chopped coriander

For the baked papadis
1. Mix the flour, oil and salt. Add water and knead into a firm dough. Knead for 2 minutes and keep aside.
2. Divide the dough into 24 portions.
3. Roll out into thin puris and prick with a fork.
4. Arrange the puris on a lightly greased baking tray.
5. Bake in a hot oven at 200°C (400°F) for 10 minutes.

For the tamatar ki chutney
1. Blanch the tomatoes in hot water. Peel and purée in a liquidiser.
2. Heat the oil in a pan, add the ajwain and asafoetida and sauté for 30 seconds.
3. Add the garlic and sauté for a few seconds.
4. Add the tomatoes, chilli powder and salt and simmer for 10 to 15 minutes or till the oil has separated. Cool and use as required.

How to proceed
1. Arrange the papadis on a serving plate.

2. Top each papadi with 1 tsp of the corn topping.
3. Put 1 tsp of the tamatar ki chutney on each papadi and garnish with the sev, pomegranate and chopped coriander.
   Serve immediately.

Handy tip: You can refrigerate the tamatar ki chutney in an air-tight container for upto 2 weeks.

∽ Vegetable Au Gratin ∽

| HIGH CAL : | 185 cal. per serving ◆ 10.8 gm. fat per serving |

This is a baked dish made with vegetables which contains a wealth of nutrients. But the use of liberal amounts of butter and cheese counteracts the effect of these nutritious vegetables and loads it with unnecessary excess calories.

Preparation time: 20 minutes.   Cooking time: 40 minutes.   Serves 4.
Baking time: 15 to 20 minutes.   Baking temperature: 200°C (400°F).

2 cups chopped and boiled mixed vegetables (carrots, peas, French beans)

For the white sauce
2 tbsp butter
½ tsp grated garlic
2 tbsp refined flour (maida)
1½ cups milk
¼ cup grated cheese
salt and pepper to taste

For the topping
½ cup grated cheese

For the white sauce
1. Heat the butter in a pan and sauté the garlic for 1 to 2 seconds.
2. Add the flour and sauté for 2 to 3 minutes.
3. Add the milk gradually, stirring continuously so that lumps do not form. Add ½ cup of water and mix well.
4. Bring to a boil, add the cheese, salt and pepper and mix well.

How to proceed
1. Combine the vegetables with the white sauce and mix well.
2. Pour into an oven-proof bowl and sprinkle the cheese on top.

3. Bake in a pre-heated oven at 200°C (400°F) for 10 to 15 minutes till the cheese melts and is lightly browned.
   Serve hot, with warm garlic bread.

Low Calorie Vegetable Au Gratin

LOW CAL : 100 cal. per serving ❖ 4.2 gm. fat per serving

A healthy version of Vegetable Au Gratin. The veggies are cooked in a creamy sauce in which the creamy texture is retained by the use of low calorie white sauce made with cauliflower purée instead of the high fat butter. Small portions of such healthy main courses can support weight loss by taking of the edge off your appetite so you won't overeat at mealtimes.

Preparation time: 10 minutes.   Cooking time: 15 minutes.   Serves 4.

2 cups chopped and boiled mixed vegetables (carrots, peas, French beans)
½ cup chopped onions
1 green chilli, chopped
1 tsp butter

1 cup low calorie white sauce, recipe below
salt and pepper to taste

For the low calorie white sauce
1½ cups chopped cauliflower or bottle gourd (lauki / doodhi)
1 tbsp butter
1 tbsp whole wheat flour (gehun ka atta)
1 cup low fat milk, page 117
salt and pepper to taste

For the topping
2 tbsp grated cheese

For the low calorie white sauce
1. Boil the cauliflower in 2 cups of water until soft. Blend in a liquidiser and strain.
2. Heat the butter in a pan, add the whole wheat flour and sauté for a few seconds.
3. Add the milk and cauliflower purée and bring to a boil while stirring the mixture continuously till it becomes thick.
4. Add salt and pepper and bring to a boil. Keep aside.

How to proceed

1. Heat the butter in a pan and sauté the onions for ½ minute.
2. Add the green chilli and sauté again for ½ minute.
3. Add the vegetables, white sauce, salt and pepper and mix well.
4. Bring to a boil and pour into a greased baking dish.
5. Top with the grated cheese and bake in a pre-heated oven at 200°C (400°F) till the cheese melts.

Serve hot.

Pav Bhaji

HIGH CAL : 574 cal. per serving ◆ 23.5 gm. fat per serving

A spicy blend of vegetables in a tomato gravy served with bread that is cooked with butter. 574 calories per serving can be reduced to mere 109 calories per serving by trimming of the visible fat from butter and substituting it with other flavourful ingredients as I've done in the recipe of Moong Sprouts Pav Bhaji, page 83

Preparation time: 15 minutes.   Cooking time: 20 minutes.   Serves 4.

For the pav
8 laddi pavs (small squares of white bread)
4 tbsp butter
1 tsp pav bhaji masala (optional)

For the bhaji
1 cup potatoes, boiled and mashed
½ cup finely chopped cauliflower
½ cup green peas
½ cup chopped carrots
1 cup chopped onions
½ cup finely chopped capsicum
2½ cups chopped tomatoes
½ tsp turmeric powder (haldi)
½ tsp chilli powder
1½ tbsp pav bhaji masala
½ tsp black salt (sanchal), optional
6 tbsp butter
salt to taste

To be ground into a chilli-garlic paste

3 to 4 Kashmiri chillies, soaked in warm water
4 to 6 large cloves garlic

For serving

1 cup chopped onions
4 lemon wedges
1 tbsp chopped coriander

For the bhaji

1. Boil the cauliflower, peas and carrots in some water till they are soft. Drain out the excess water.
2. Heat the butter in a large pan, add the onions and capsicum and sauté for 2 minutes. Then, add the prepared chilli-garlic paste and sauté till the onions soften.
3. Add the tomatoes and simmer till the oil separates.
4. Add the turmeric powder, chilli powder, pav bhaji masala, black salt and salt and cook for 2 to 3 minutes.
5. Add the boiled vegetables and potatoes. Mash the potatoes thoroughly using a potato masher, adding ½ cup of water if required.

For the pav

1. Slice each pav into 2 horizontally. Apply a little butter to each side and sprinkle a little pav bhaji masala, if desired.
2. Heat a tava (griddle) and cook the pav on both sides till the pieces are lightly browned.

How to proceed

1. Spoon the hot bhaji on 4 individual plates and top with the onions and coriander.
2. Serve with hot pav and lemon wedges.

Moong Sprouts Pav Bhaji

LOW CAL :	109 cal. per serving ❖ 1.0 gm. fat per serving

Enliven your favourite snack by adding a handful of moong sprouts to the pav bhaji and reducing the use of butter. This nutrient rich dish is easy to digest due to the addition of sprouts and is also rich in flavour.

Preparation time: 10 minutes.   Cooking time: 10 minutes.   Serves 4.

8 laddi pav (small squares of white bread)
2 cups moong sprouts
1 cup potatoes, boiled and mashed
1 cup finely chopped and boiled mixed vegetables (carrots, cauliflower, green peas)
¾ cup chopped onions
1 cup chopped tomatoes
½ tsp chilli powder
½ tsp turmeric powder (haldi)
1 green chilli, chopped
1 tbsp pav bhaji masala
1 tsp butter
1 tsp oil
2 tbsp chopped coriander
salt to taste

1. Boil the moong sprouts in very little water. Do not overcook. Drain and keep the moong water aside.
2. Heat the oil and butter in a large tava (griddle) and sauté the onions until golden brown.
3. Then add the tomatoes, chilli powder, turmeric powder, green chilli, pav bhaji masala and salt and cook for 1 minute.

4. Add the potatoes, moong sprouts, mixed boiled vegetables and coriander and cook for 2 minutes.
5. If the mixture becomes dry, sprinkle the moong water on top. Serve hot with pav.

Handy tip : To add a health touch further, serve this bhaji with brown bread.

～ Vegetable Frankie ～

HIGH CAL :	584 cal. per frankie ◆ 31.9 gm. fat per frankie

A mouthwatering snack. Once you have tasted it, you will always ask for more. But did you know that 1 frankie has approximately 584 calories ! To make it a low fat feast, make sure you load it with fibre and nutrient rich vegetables. Turn to page 88, for a more healthy chat-pata recipe.

Preparation time: 30 minutes.   Cooking time: 20 minutes.   Makes 4 frankies.

For the puris
1 cup refined flour (maida)
1 slice white bread
¼ tsp salt
½ tbsp ghee (optional)

ghee for deep frying

For the potato rolls
1½ cups potatoes, boiled and mashed
½ cup green peas, boiled and mashed
½ cup grated cheese
2 green chillies, chopped
½ tsp garam masala
½ tsp lemon juice
salt to taste
⅓ cup refined flour (maida) mixed with ½ cup of water
bread crumbs for coating
oil for deep frying

To be mixed into masala water
1 tsp amchur (dry mango powder)
½ tsp chilli powder
¼ tsp garam masala
¼ tsp salt
2 tbsp water

To be mixed into an onion masala mixture
½ cup chopped onions
½ tsp chilli powder
½ tsp amchur (dry mango powder)
¼ tsp salt

Other ingredients
green chillies in vinegar

For the puris
1. Sieve the refined flour.
2. Soak the bread slice in water for a few minutes. Squeeze out the water and crumble thoroughly.
3. Add the crumbled bread, salt and ghee to the flour and make a dough by adding water. Divide the dough into 4 equal parts.
4. Roll out into thick puris and deep fry very lightly in ghee. Alternatively, roll out into thin puris and cook each puri on a tava (griddle) using ghee on both sides for a few seconds.

For the potato rolls
1. Mix the potatoes, green peas, cheese, chillies, garam masala, lemon juice and salt and shape into long rolls of the size of the puris.

2. Dip the rolls in the refined flour batter and roll in the bread crumbs.
3. Deep fry in hot oil till they are golden brown. Drain.

How to proceed
1. On a small tava (griddle), cook each puri on both sides for few minutes.
2. On each puri, apply a little masala water, sprinkle a little onion masala mixture and chillies in vinegar.
3. Place a potato roll in the centre and roll the puri over to make a cylindrical shape. Serve immediately.
4. Repeat with the remaining ingredients to make 3 more frankies.

⁓ Chat-Pati Frankie ⁓

LOW CAL : 221 cal. per frankie ◆ 2.3 gm. fat per frankie

Relish this frankie that has only half the calories of the previous recipe. Make mealtimes happy and healthy by using cooking methods like roasting instead of deep frying as shown in this recipe.

Preparation time: 20 minutes.   Cooking time: 15 minutes.   Makes 4 frankies.

4 whole wheat chapaties
1½ cups potatoes, boiled and mashed
½ cup grated low fat paneer (cottage cheese), page 118
½ cup peeled and grated carrot
1 cheese cube, grated
2 tsp chaat masala
1 tbsp lemon juice
½ cup tomatoes, cut into strips
¼ cup capsicum, cut into strips
salt to taste

1. Combine the paneer, carrot, cheese, half the chaat masala, lemon juice and salt and mix well.
2. Divide into 4 equal parts and roll each part into a long roll of the size of chapaties. Keep aside.
3. Warm the chapaties and place on a serving plate.
4. Put one roll of the potato and paneer mixture in the centre of a chapati.
5. Put some capsicum and tomato strips and sprinkle some chaat masala on top.
6. Roll up the chapati to make a cylindrical shape.
7. Repeat with the remaining ingredients to make 3 more frankies.
   Serve immediately.

Canneloni - Neapolitan Style

HIGH CAL : 434 cal. per serving ◆ 16.9 gm. fat per serving

Very often we impress our guests with this robust Italian pasta dish baked in tomato sauce and cheese. You would be surprised to know that one serving of this dish provides 434 calories against its low fat version which adds upto only 190 calories per serving. To minimize your caloric intake, check out the low calorie version of canneloni on page 93.

Preparation time: 20 minutes.   Cooking time: 40 minutes.   Serves 4.
Baking time: 15 minutes.   Baking temperature: 200°C (400°F).

For the pasta
¾ cup refined flour (maida)
4 tsp oil
½ tsp salt

For the stuffing
1 cup potatoes, boiled and mashed
¼ cup chopped onions
½ tsp chopped garlic
½ cup diced and boiled French beans

¼ cup diced and boiled carrots
½ cup boiled green peas
4 tbsp tomato ketchup
1 tsp chilli powder
¼ tsp dried oregano
1 tbsp oilve oil
salt to taste

For the sauce
4 cups roughly chopped tomatoes
½ cup chopped onions
5 cloves garlic, crushed
4 tbsp sugar (approx.)
½ tsp chilli powder
½ cup grated cooking cheese
¼ tsp dried oregano
2 tbsp oil
salt to taste

For the topping
¾ cup grated cooking cheese

For the pasta
1. Mix the flour, 1 tsp of oil and salt. Add water and knead into a semi-soft dough.
2. Keep the dough for 1 hour covered with a damp muslin cloth. Thereafter, divide the dough into 4 equal parts.
3. Roll out each portion of the dough into small thin circles.
4. Boil plenty of water in a vessel and add 3 tsp of oil to the boiling water.
5. Drop one round at a time into the boiling water, cook for ½ minute and transfer into cold water. Repeat for all the remaining circles. Just before use, drain out and discard the water.

For the stuffing
1. Heat the oil in a pan, add the onions and garlic and sauté for 2 to 3 minutes.
2. Add the boiled vegetables, mashed potatoes, tomato ketchup, chilli powder and salt and cook for 2 minutes.

For the sauce
1. Add ½ cup of water to the tomatoes and simmer till they are soft. Cool and make a purée by passing through a strainer.
2. Heat the oil in a pan, add the onions and sauté for a few seconds in a pan. Add the crushed garlic and sauté for a few more seconds.
3. Add the tomato purée, sugar, chilli powder and salt and simmer for 15 minutes.

Add the cheese and dried oregano and mix well.

How to proceed
1. Fill each pasta circle with a tbsp of the stuffing and roll up.
2. Arrange all the filled pasta on a greased baking dish, pour hot tomato sauce and sprinkle the cheese on top.
3. Bake in a pre-heated oven at 200 °C (400°F) for 10 minutes.
   Serve hot.

Handy tip: You can also use ready made lasagne sheets. Cook them as per the instructions on the packet and fill with the stuffing mixture.

Low Calorie Canneloni

LOW CAL : 190 cal. per serving ◆ 4.4 gm. fat per serving

A *well-balanced main dish with an Italian flavour using low fat paneer for protein and whole wheat flour and vegetables for minerals, vitamins and fibre. This party favourite recipe is more appealing in its fat free form and I am sure you will enjoy it more.*

93

Preparation time: 20 minutes.   Cooking time: 30 minutes.   Serves 4.
Baking time: 15 minutes.   Baking temperature: 200°C (400°F).

For the pasta
¼ cup whole wheat flour (gehun ka atta)
2 tsp oil
salt to taste

For the stuffing
1½ cups finely chopped mixed boiled vegetables
½ recipe low fat paneer (cottage cheese), page 118
¼ cup chopped onions
1 tsp chilli powder
1 tsp oil
salt to taste

For the tomato sauce
3 cups chopped tomatoes
¼ cup chopped onions
2 cloves garlic, crushed
½ tsp chilli powder

½ tsp mixed dried herbs
1 tsp sugar (optional)
2 tsp oil
salt to taste

For the topping
2 tbsp grated low fat paneer (cottage cheese), page 118

For the pasta
1. Mix the whole wheat flour, oil and salt. Add water and prepare a soft dough.
2. Keep the dough aside for 1 hour, covered with a damp muslin cloth. Divide the dough into 4 equal parts.
3. Roll out the dough into small thin circles of 100 mm. to 125 mm. (4" to 5") diameter.
4. Boil plenty of water in a vessel.
5. Drop one circle of dough at a time into the boiling water, cook for ½ minute and remove. Transfer into a pan of cold water.
6. Repeat for the remaining circles. Just before use, drain and discard the water.

For the stuffing
1. Heat the oil and sauté the onions for ½ minute.
2. Add the remaining ingredients and cook for 1 more minute. Keep aside.

For the tomato sauce
1. Heat the oil in a pan and sauté the onions and garlic for 1 minute.
2. Add the tomatoes and cook until soft. Cool and blend in a liquidiser.
3. Add the chilli powder, mixed herbs, sugar and salt and simmer for 2 to 3 minutes.

How to proceed
1. Fill each pasta circle with 1 tbsp of the stuffing and roll up like a pancake.
2. Arrange the canneloni on a greased baking dish and pour the tomato sauce on top.
3. Sprinkle the paneer on top and bake in a pre-heated oven at 200°C (400°F) for 10 minutes.
   Serve hot.

Vada Pav

The Indian burger. It's the quickest and easiest meal or snack available on the street corners of Mumbai. Hot, spicy and delicious, it's one snack I can never resist especially on a rainy day. But it's also quite high in calories, so I have found a less guilty version of enjoying my favourite snack Turn over to page 100, and discover my healthy variation.

Preparation time: 10 minutes.   Cooking time: 30 minutes.   Makes 8 vada pavs.

8 laddi pavs (small squares of white bread)
4 tbsp dry garlic chutney

For the vada filling
3 cups boiled and mashed potatoes
3 to 4 green chillies, chopped
1 tsp chopped ginger
1½ tsp chopped garlic
1 tsp mustard seeds (rai)
¼ tsp asafoetida (hing)

6 to 8 curry leaves
¼ tsp turmeric powder (haldi)
1½ tsp oil
salt to taste

For the outer covering
¾ cup Bengal gram flour (besan)
¼ tsp turmeric powder (haldi)
a pinch soda bi-carb
1 tsp oil
salt to taste

Other ingredients
oil for deep frying

For the vada filling
1. Pound the green chillies, ginger and garlic using a mortar and pestle.
2. Heat the oil in a pan and add the mustard seeds. When they crackle, add the asafoetida and curry leaves and sauté for a few seconds.
3. Add the pounded mixture and sauté again for a few seconds. Add the potatoes, turmeric powder and salt and mix well.

4. Remove from the fire and cool.
5. Divide into 8 equal portions. Shape into rounds.

For the outer covering
1. Combine all the ingredients in a bowl and make a batter using approx. 1/3 cup of water.
2. Dip each round of the vada filling into the batter and allow it to coat the mixture well.
3. Deep fry in hot oil till golden brown. Drain on absorbent paper and keep aside.

How to proceed
1. Slice each pav into half horizontally and spread some dry garlic chutney inside.
2. Place one vada in each pav and serve immediately.

Handy tip: Laddi pavs are small square shaped white bread rolls which are available at local bakeries. You can also use bread rolls or slices if the pav is not available.

Healthy Vada Pav

LOW CAL : 136 cal. per vada pav ❖ 3.2 gm. fat per vada pav

This recipe replaces the refined flour bread with a whole wheat pita. I have also omitted frying the vada altogether making it guilt free. The salad and chutney add fibre, crunch and flavour to this delicious snack. Feel free to make 2 or 3 recipes of the pita bread and refrigerate, so that you can enjoy it any time hunger strikes.

Preparation time: 20 minutes.   Cooking time: 15 minutes.   Makes 8 vada pavs.

For the pita bread
1 cup whole wheat flour (gehun ka atta)
1 tsp (5 grams) crumbled fresh yeast
1 tsp sugar
1 tbsp oil
½ tsp salt

For the garlic chutney
¼ cup garlic cloves
1 tbsp chilli powder
1 tsp coriander-cumin seed (dhania-jeera) powder

salt to taste

To be mixed into a vada filling
3 cups boiled and mashed potatoes
1 tbsp ginger-green chilli paste
1 tbsp chopped coriander
½ tsp turmeric powder (haldi)
salt to taste

Other ingredients
8 tomato slices
1 cup shredded lettuce
8 onion slices

For the pita bread
1. Combine all the ingredients except the oil in a bowl and knead into a soft dough using enough water until it is smooth and elastic.
2. Add the oil and knead again.
3. Cover the dough with a wet muslin cloth and allow it to prove till it doubles in volume (approx. 15 to 20 minutes).
4. Press the dough lightly to remove the air.

5. Divide the dough into 4 equal parts.
6. Roll out each portion into a circle of 125 mm. (5") diameter and 3 mm. (¼") thickness.
7. Cook the pita breads on a hot tava (griddle) on each side for a minute or until the bread puffs up.
8. Remove and keep aside.
9. Cut each pita bread into 2 halves. Keep aside. These are called pita pockets.

For the garlic chutney
Blend all the ingredients in a blender with a little water to get a smooth chutney. Keep aside.

How to proceed
1. Warm the pita bread halves on a tava (griddle) and apply some garlic chutney on the inside.
2. Divide the vada filling mixture into 8 equal portions.
3. Fill each pita bread half with one slice of tomato, some lettuce, one slice of onion and one portion of the vada filling mixture.
4. Repeat for the remaining pita bread halves and other ingredients to make 7 more healthy vada pavs.
Serve immediately.

DESERTS

Gajar Halwa

HIGH CAL : | 527 cal. per serving ❖ 24.5 gm. fat per serving

This is the traditional way of making gajar ka halwa. Who doesn't like this divine delicacy? But we often tend to avoid it, as it is full of calorie laden ingredients like khoya, ghee and dried fruits. I have specially modified this recipe, see page 104, which will never fail to satiate your sweet tooth and also help you to watch your weight.

Preparation time: 15 minutes.   Cooking time: 30 minutes.   Serves 4.

2 cups grated carrots
2 cups milk
1 cup sugar
½ cup grated khoya
1 tbsp chopped almonds
1 tbsp raisins (kismish)
½ tsp cardamom (elaichi) powder

¼ cup ghee

1. In a large pan, cook the carrots in the milk till they are soft.
2. Add the sugar and khoya and mix well.
3. Cook till the mixture leaves the sides of the pan, adding a little ghee at a time till the halwa smells fragrant.
4. Add the almonds, raisins and cardamom powder and mix well.
   Serve hot.

Handy tip: Another way of making this halwa is to first sauté the carrots in the ghee and then add the milk, khoya and sugar and to cook till it thickens.

Low Calorie Gajar Halwa

LOW CAL :	230 cal. per serving ◆ 1.6 gm. fat per serving

Carrot is a versatile vegetable in a low fat kitchen and is used to prepare this dessert in a jiffy to tantalize your taste buds. Enrich this dessert by avoiding khoya and replacing the full fat milk powder with its low fat counterpart. A pinch of cardamom powder further enhances the taste of this appealing halwa.

Preparation time: 10 minutes.   Cooking time: 15 minutes.   Serves 4.

3 cups grated carrots
½ cup sugar
5 tbsp skim milk powder
a pinch cardamom (elaichi) powder
1 tbsp slivered almonds
1 tbsp ghee

1. Steam the carrots over boiling water for 3 to 5 minutes.
2. Heat the ghee in a pan, add the steamed carrots and sauté for 2 minutes.
3. Add the sugar and cook for 2 to 3 minutes. Then add the skim milk powder and cook for a few minutes, stirring continuously.
4. Sprinkle the cardamom powder and almonds and mix well.
   Serve hot.

Kesar Malai Kulfi

HIGH CAL : 288 cal. per kulfi ◆ 13.0 gm. fat per kulfi

Rich, creamy, ice-cream made with reduced milk flavoured with cardamom and packed with calories. How about a kulfi which does not take long to prepare and provides substantial amount of calcium without excess fat and calories? See the facing page for such a fascinating variation.

Preparation time: 10 minutes.   Cooking time: 45 minutes.   Makes 5 kulfis.

1 litre full fat milk
a few strands saffron
1 tbsp arrowroot or cornflour
⅓ cup sugar
¼ tsp cardamom (elaichi) powder

1. In a small bowl, soak the saffron in a little warm milk and keep aside.
2. Dissolve the arrowroot in 2 tablespoons of water and keep aside.
3. Put the milk in a broad non-stick pan and bring it to a boil.
4. Add the arrowroot solution and sugar and mix well.

5. Simmer over a medium flame, stirring continuously till the milk reduces to a little less than half the original quantity (approx. 450 ml.).
6. Cool completely, add the cardamom powder and saffron mixture and mix well.
7. Pour into kulfi moulds and freeze overnight or till it sets.
8. To unmould, allow the moulds to remain outside the refrigerator for 5 minutes and then unmould by inserting a wooden skewer stick or a fork in the centre of the kulfi and pulling it out.

Low Fat Kulfi with Strawberry Sauce

LOW CAL :	99 cal. per kulfi ❖ 0 gm. fat per kulfi

This is a dessert which has always gained praise from all my family members. Citric acid added to the milk causes the milk to split and gives it the creamy texture which is characteristic to kulfi. Almost nil in fat and minimal in calories, this frozen dessert is extremely eye appealing. You will never be able to tell the difference.

Preparation time: 10 minutes.   Cooking time: 40 minutes.   Makes 5 kulfis.

1 litre low fat milk, page 117
a pinch citric acid crystals
1 tsp cornflour
6 tsp sugar
a few saffron strands
¼ tsp cardamom (elaichi) powder

To be mixed together for the strawberry sauce
½ cup crushed strawberry
4 tsp powdered sugar

1. In a small bowl, soak the saffron in a little warm milk and keep aside.
2. Dissolve the cornflour in 1 tbsp of milk and keep aside.
3. Dissolve the citric acid in 2 tbsp of water and keep aside.
4. Put the milk in a broad non-stick pan and bring to a boil.
5. Simmer over a medium flame stirring continuously till the milk reduces to a little more than half the original quantity (approx. 600 ml.).
6. Add the citric acid solution and simmer for 2 minutes. The milk may appear curdled, but that is intended.
7. Add the cornflour solution and sugar and bring to a boil. Simmer for 5 to 7 minutes.

8. Cool completely. Add the saffron mixture and powder and mix well.
9. Pour into a shallow container and freeze till slushy (approx. 3 to 4 hours).
10. Remove and blend in a blender to break all the ice crystals till the kulfi is smooth and creamy.
11. Pour into 5 kulfi moulds and freeze overnight or until it sets.
12. To unmould, allow the moulds to remain outside the refrigerator for 5 minutes and then unmould by inserting a wooden skewer stick or a fork in the centre of the kulfi and pulling it out.
13. Serve topped with the strawberry sauce.

⌇ Quick Rabdi ⌇

HIGH CAL :	361 cal. per serving ◆ 13.3 gm. fat per serving

Milk is thickened with fresh bread crumbs to give you an instant rabdi. This is not the original recipe but one that's used to make a really creamy rabdi in a jiffy.

Preparation time: 10 minutes.   Cooking time: 45 minutes.   Makes 5 kulfis.

3 cups full fat milk

2 bread slices
½ cup condensed milk
2 tbsp sugar (optional)
¼ tsp cardamom (elaichi) powder
a few saffron strands

1. Remove the crusts of the bread slices and discard. Grind the bread slices in a food processor to make fresh bread crumbs. Keep aside.
2. Bring the milk to a boil in a heavy bottomed pan. Add the fresh bread crumbs, condensed milk and sugar and cook over a medium flame, while stirring continuously (approx. 10 minutes).
3. Dissolve the saffron in 1 tbsp of warm water and keep aside.
4. Remove from the fire, add the cardamom powder and saffron and mix well.
5. Refrigerate for 2 to 3 hours and serve chilled.

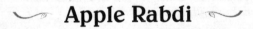

Apple Rabdi

LOW CAL : 216 cal. per serving ❖ 1.1 gm. fat per serving

Apples are great to have when on a weight loss programme. Try them with their peels, while preparing this dish as much of their goodness (all vitamins, minerals and fibre) lies just beneath 110

their skin. Though I have used apples in this rabdi, you can use whatever fruit strikes your fancy the day you make it. Try fruits like pears and peaches.

Preparation time: 5 minutes.   Cooking time: 20 minutes.   Serves 4.

1 litre low fat milk, page 117
3 tbsp sugar
2 dessert apples, grated
½ tsp cardamom (elaichi) powder
3 almonds, blanched and sliced

1. Put the milk in a broad non-stick vessel and simmer for 10 to 12 minutes.
2. Add the sugar and cook on a slow flame while stirring continuously, until the mixture reduces to half.
3. Add the apples to the milk and bring to a boil and remove from the heat at once. Sprinkle almonds and cardamom powder on top. Refrigerate and serve chilled.

Note : If the apples are a little sharp, increase the quantity of sugar.

∽ Sinful Lemon Cheesecake ∽

HIGH CAL :	339 cal. per serving ◆ 20.1 gm. fat per serving

The crisp base of this elegant dessert is filled with rich cream cheese and topped with a bold lemon flavoured sauce. However, an occasional treat of this creamy cake provides 339 calories as compared to its low calorie version, page 115, which adds on only 168 calories to your menu.

Preparation time: 10 minutes.   Cooking time: 5 minutes.   Serves 6.
Setting time: 1 hour.

For the biscuit base
1 cup crushed digestive biscuits
½ cup melted butter

For the filling
½ cup (100 gms) cream
juice of 1½ lemons
1 tsp grated lemon rind
1 cup cream cheese, page 119

½ cup powdered sugar
½ tsp lemon essence

For the lemon sauce
3 tbsp sugar
1 tsp cornflour
¾ tbsp lemon juice
½ tsp grated lemon rind
2 drops lemon essence
a drop of lemon yellow colour (optional)
½ tsp butter

For the biscuit base
1. Mix the biscuit crumbs with the melted butter and press the mixture into the base of a 175 mm. (7") loose bottomed pie dish.
2. Chill until firm.

For the filling
1. Whisk the cream in a clean dry bowl till soft peaks form. Keep aside.
2. Mix the lemon rind, lemon juice, cream cheese, sugar and lemon essence till it is smooth.

3. Fold in the whipped cream gently so that it does not curdle or split.
4. Spread this filling over the set biscuit base and chill until firm.

For the lemon sauce
1. Combine the sugar with ½ cup of water in a saucepan and heat till the sugar is dissolved.
2. Dissolve the cornflour in 2 tbsp of water and add it to the sugar syrup.
3. Heat, stirring continuously, till the mixture thickens and gets a coating consistency. Add the butter and mix well.
4. Cool and add the lemon juice, lemon rind, lemon essence and lemon yellow colour. Mix well and keep aside. Cool completely while stirring continuously.

How to proceed
1. Unmould the cheesecake and place on a serving plate.
2. Pour the lemon sauce on top and refrigerate again.
   Serve chilled.

Handy tip: The best way to crush biscuits is to put them in a plastic bag or use a tea towel and crush using both hands till you get medium sized crumbs.

Guilt Free Lemon Cheesecake

Picture on back cover.

LOW CAL :	168 cal. per serving ✦ 5.0 gm. fat per serving

Cheesecakes need not always be fattening to be delicious. By substituting full fat milk with its low fat version and full fat cream with low fat cream cheese along with a reduction in the amount of sugar, you can cut down the intake of calories. But the trick while watching your waistline is to watch the portion size too. Serve yourself a small portion, put the rest aside and savour your treat.

Preparation time: 15 minutes.   Cooking time: 15 minutes.   Serves 6.
Setting time: 1 hour.

For the crust
14 digestive biscuits, crushed
2 tsp melted low fat butter

For the cheesecake mixture
1 recipe low fat cream cheese, page 121
½ cup low fat curds, page 118
½ cup powdered sugar
1 tsp lemon juice

1 tsp grated lemon rind
½ tsp lemon essence

For the topping
2 tbsp sugar free orange marmalade

For the crust
1. Combine the butter and biscuits and line the bottom of a 150 mm. (6") diameter loose bottomed cake tin with it.
2. Refrigerate till set.

For the cheesecake mixture
1. Blend the cream cheese in a blender till it is smooth and free of lumps, adding some warm milk or whey if required.
2. Combine with the remaining ingredients in a bowl and whisk till it is a smooth mixture.

For the topping
Combine the marmalade with 1 tbsp of water in a pan and melt over gentle heat. Cool slightly.

How to proceed
1. Pour the cheesecake mixture over the set crust and refrigerate till the mixture sets.
2. Pour the topping over and chill again for 10 to 15 minutes.
3. Cut into wedges and serve chilled.

BASIC RECIPES

 Low Fat Milk

LOW CAL : 71 cal. per cup ◆ 0 gm. fat per cup

This low fat milk has been made using skim milk powder and is virtually fat free while having all the goodness of milk like protein, calcium and vitamin B. Skim milk powder is easily available at all leading grocery stores. Alternatively, feel free to use 99% fat free milk (low fat milk) readily available in tetrapacks at most grocery stores. This low fat milk gives you only 71 calories per cup as compared to 234 calories per cup (along with 13 grams of fat) from full fat milk. So, use low fat milk to prepare milkshakes, desserts and for virtually any recipe where milk is used.

Preparation time: 5 minutes.   Cooking time: 7 minutes.   Makes 1 litre (5 cups).

100 grams (1 cup) skim milk powder
1 litre water

1. Mix the skim milk powder in 1½ cups of water and make a smooth paste.
2. Add the remaining water and if desired, mix with a whisk.
3. Boil and use as required.

Note : Each packet of skim milk has its own method of preparation.

~ Low Fat Curds ~

LOW CAL : 71 cal. per cup ◆ 0 gm. fat per cup

Curds are a nutritious addition to our diet as they are easier to digest than milk. Curds complement the protein present in cereals and make it a complete protein, when accompanied with dishes like parathas, biryanis etc Use this low fat version of curds as an accompaniment to a main meal or in raitas, salad dressings etc. to enjoy all the goodness of curds without the fat.

Preparation time: 5 minutes.   Cooking time: 3 minutes.   Makes 5 cups.

1 litre low fat milk, page 117
1 tbsp curds

1. Warm the milk.
2. Add the curds, mix well and cover.
3. Keep aside until the curds set (approx. 5 to 6 hours).
4. During the cold climate, place inside a casserole or closed oven to set.

Handy tip : Curds set quickly in a warm and dark place.

~ Low Fat Paneer ~

LOW CAL : 214 cal. per ¾ cup ◆ 0.1 gm. fat per ¾ cup

This paneer is made using skim milk that has all the goodness of milk without the fat. For milk fussy adults, this is a 118 *superb way of adding protein (necessary for maintenance of body cells) and calcium (necessary for healthy bones) to their diet.*

Preparation time: 30 minutes.   Setting time: 10 minutes.   Makes 100 grams
(approx. ¼ cup).

2 cups low fat milk, page 117
1 cup low fat curds, page 118, beaten

1. Put the milk to boil in a broad pan. When it starts boiling, add the curds and mix well.
2. Remove from the heat and stir gently until the milk curdles.
3. Strain and tie the curdled milk in a muslin cloth. Hang for about half an hour to allow the whey to drain out. Use as required.

Note : If the milk has not curdled completely at step 2, allow the milk to boil once more.

Handy tip :   If you want firm paneer, cover the block of paneer with a heavy weight to compress it. This way you will be able to cut cubes from the paneer.

Cream Cheese

| HIGH CAL : | 1170 cal. per cup   ◆   65.0 gm. fat per cup |

Cream cheese is a type of cheese spread available abroad in most supermarkets. Since it is not very easily available in India, I have made it using fresh milk. As a cup of cream cheese is absolutely calorie and fat laden, I tried using low 119 *fat milk. Its low fat version, see facing page, is sure to suit your palate and avoid adding those excess kilos too.*

Preparation time: a few minutes.   Setting time: 10 minutes.   Makes 1 cup approx.

1 litre full fat milk
1 tsp citric acid crystals
½ cup warm water

1. Put the milk to boil in a thick bottomed pan.
2. When it comes to a boil, remove from the flame and keep aside for a few minutes.
3. In another bowl, mix the citric acid crystals with the warm water.
4. Pour a little of this mixture into the hot milk and allow it to stand for about 5 minutes till the milk curdles on its own. Stir gently if required. Add some more citric acid liquid if required.
5. Strain this mixture using a muslin cloth, leaving some of the whey in the curdled mixture.
6. Blend the drained milk solids in a food processor till thick and creamy. Refrigerate till chill use as required.

Handy tips : 1. If the drained whey is milky, boil it once more and strain the separated milk solids.
2. You can also use ½ tbsp of lemon juice instead of the citric acid crystals.

Low Fat Cream Cheese

LOW CAL : 357 cal. per cup ◆ 0.1 gm. fat per cup

Being made from low fat milk, this cream cheese is absolutely fat free and can be relished without any guilt even by diabetics with high blood sugar levels and individuals with high blood sugar levels. Use this cream cheese to make delectable desserts (as I have done in the recipe of Guilt Free Lemon Cheesecake, page 115) or even to make delectable dips to serve at parties along with vegetable crudités.

Preparation time: a few minutes.   Setting time: 10 minutes.   Makes 1 cup approx.

1 litre low fat milk, page 117
1 tsp citric acid crystals
½ cup warm water

1. Put the milk to boil in a thick bottomed pan.
2. When it comes to a boil, remove from the flame and keep aside for a few minutes.
3. In another bowl, mix the citric acid crystals with the warm water.
4. Pour a little of this mixture into the hot milk and allow it to stand for about 5 minutes till the milk curdles on its own. Stir gently if required. Add some more citric acid if required.
5. Strain this mixture using a muslin cloth, leaving some of the whey in the curdled mixture.
6. Blend the drained milk solids in a food processor till thick and creamy.
   Refrigerate and use as required.

Handy tips : As per previous recipe.

CALORIE COUNTER

A calorie (commonly called as kilocalorie) is the energy obtained from all foods - whether solid or liquid. The only food that does not provide us energy is water. Calories fuel our body and help us to perform our day-to-day activities. However, consuming more calories than our body needs, whether they come from carbohydrates, protein or fat will be stored as fat in the body, which will ultimately end up as weight gain.

Flip the pages, for a comprehensive calorie counter inclusive of the fat count of all basic ingredients that are found on most kitchen shelves.

So, the next time you want to know how many calories your favourite food contains, all you have to do is look up this handy calorie counter.

You can also email us at tarla@tarladalal.com for more information.

Flours and Rice

Ingredients	Measure	Calories (kcal)	Fat (gm)
Rice flour (*chawal ka atta*)	1 cup	414	0.6
Plain flour (*maida*)	1 cup	383	1.0
Ragi flour (*nachni ka atta*)	1 cup	374	1.5
Wheat flour (*gehun ka atta*)	1 cup	368	1.8
Bajra flour (*black millet flour*)	1 cup	347	4.8
Jowar flour (*white millet flour*)	1 cup	342	1.9
Bengal gram flour (*besan*)	1 cup	305	4.6
Soyabean flour	1 cup	294	13.3
Rice, long grain	1 cup, cooked	197	0.3
Rice, short grain	1 cup, cooked	197	0.3
Maize flour (*makai ka atta*)	1 cup	118	0.8
Wheat bran	1 tbsp.	42	0.6

All the ingredients are arranged according to the descending order of their caloric count and the values are given for a standard cup (200 ml.) and tablespoon (15 ml.).

Breakfasts and Snacks

Ingredients	Measure	Calories (kcal)	Fat (gm)
Sago	1 cup	534	0.1
Broken wheat *(dalia)*	1 cup	527	2.4
Semolina *(rawa)*	1 cup	487	1.1
Quick cooking rolled oats	1 cup	277	5.6
Poha *(beaten rice flakes)*	1 cup	208	0.7
Vermicelli *(sevaiiyan)*	1 cup	123	0.1
Corn flakes	1 cup	98	0.1
Bread slice, *brown*	1 no.	49	0.2
Bread slice, *white*	1 no.	49	0.1
Puffed rice *(mumara)*	1 cup	46	0.0

All the ingredients are arranged according to the descending order of their caloric count and the values are given for a standard cup (200 ml.) and tablespoon (15 ml.).

Pulses

Ingredients	Measure	Calories (kcal)	Fat (gm)
Soyabean	1 cup, cooked	307	13.8
Chana dal *(split Bengal gram)*	1 cup, cooked	305	4.6
Moong dal *(split green gram)*	1 cup, cooked	303	1.0
Chick peas *(kabuli chana)*	1 cup, cooked	295	4.3
Toovar *(arhar)* **dal**	1 cup, cooked	275	1.4
Masoor dal *(split red lentils)*	1 cup, cooked	261	0.5
Urad dal *(split black lentils)*	1 cup, cooked	260	1.1
Chawli *(cow peas)*	1 cup, cooked	258	0.8
Matki *(moath beans)*	1 cup, cooked	191	0.6
Vaal *(field beans)*	1 cup, cooked	187	0.4
Moong *(green gram)*	1 cup, cooked	177	0.7
Red chana *(whole red gram)*	1 cup, cooked	176	1.5
Rajma *(kidney beans)*	1 cup, cooked	166	0.6

All the ingredients are arranged according to the descending order of their caloric count and the values are given for a standard cup (200 ml.) and tablespoon (15 ml.).

Vegetables (a) Roots and Tubers

Ingredients	Measure	Calories (kcal)	Fat (gm)
Kand *(purple yam)*	1 cup, chopped	133	0.1
Suran *(yam)*	1 cup, chopped	101	0.1
Potato	1 cup, chopped	89	0.1
Onion	1 cup, chopped	66	0.1
Beetroot	1 cup, chopped	32	0.1
Red pumpkin *(kaddu)*	1 cup, chopped	32	0.1
Carrot	1 cup, chopped	27	0.1
Radish *(mooli)*	1 cup, chopped	20	0.1
Spring onion	1 cup, chopped	15	0.1

All the ingredients are arranged according to the descending order of their caloric count and the values are given for a standard cup (200 ml.) and tablespoon (15 ml.).

(b) Leafy Vegetables

Ingredients	Measure	Calories (kcal)	Fat (gm)
Chawli *(cow pea)* **leaves**	1 cup, chopped	26	0.5
Colocasia leaves	1 cup, chopped	25	0.7
Spinach *(palak)*	1 cup, chopped	18	0.5
Fenugreek *(methi)* **leaves**	1 cup, chopped	14	0.3
Mint leaves	1 cup, chopped	14	0.2
Coriander leaves	1 cup, chopped	11	0.2
Dill *(shepu)*	1 cup, chopped	07	0.1

All the ingredients are arranged according to the descending order of their caloric count and the values are given for a standard cup (200 ml.) and tablespoon (15 ml.).

(c) Everyday Vegetables

Ingredients	Measure	Calories (kcal)	Fat (gm)
Green peas	1 cup	130	0.1
Drumsticks	1 cup, chopped	42	0.2
Tomato	1 cup, chopped	31	0.3
Brinjal *(baingan)*	1 cup, chopped	30	0.4
Capsicum	1 cup, chopped	29	0.4
Karela *(bitter gourd)*	1 cup, chopped	28	0.2
Tendli	1 cup, chopped	26	0.2
French beans	1 cup, chopped	26	0.1
Bhindi *(ladies finger)*	1 cup, chopped	25	0.1
Cauliflower	1 cup, florets	22	0.3
Cabbage	1 cup, shredded	22	0.1
Cluster beans *(gavarfali)*	1 cup, chopped	16	0.4
Cucumber	1 cup, chopped	16	0.1
Turai *(ridge gourd)*	1 cup, chopped	15	0.1
Bottle gourd *(lauki / doodhi)*	1 cup, chopped	13	0.1

All the ingredients are arranged according to the descending order of their caloric count and the values are given for a standard cup (200 ml.) and tablespoon (15 ml.).

(b) Exotic Vegetables

Ingredients	Measure	Calories (kcal)	Fat (gm)
Corn (*makai*), *fresh*	1 cup, grated	330	2.4
Sweet corn	1 cup, chopped	122	0.1
Baby corn	1 cup	122	0.1
Celery stalk	1 cup, chopped	20	0.1
Asparagus	1 cup, chopped	16	0.5
Mushrooms, *fresh*	1 cup, sliced	16	0.3
Lettuce	1 cup, shredded	15	0.4
Broccoli	1 cup, florets	14	0.2

All the ingredients are arranged according to the descending order of their caloric count and the values are given for a standard cup (200 ml.) and tablespoon (15 ml.).

Fruits

Ingredients	Measure	Calories (kcal)	Fat (gm)
Banana	1 cup, chopped	348	0.9
Custard apple	1 cup, pulp	187	0.7
Chickoo	1 cup, chopped	129	1.5
Jamun, *black*	1 cup, chopped	124	0.6
Jamun, *white*	1 cup, chopped	112	0.5
Cherry	1 cup, chopped	110	0.9
Mango	1 cup, chopped	104	0.6
Grapes	1 cup	99	0.4
Pomegranate *(anar)*	1 cup	94	0.1
Orange	1 cup, segments	84	0.4
Pineapple	1 cup, chopped	76	0.2
Sweet lime	1 cup, segments	76	0.5
Plums	1 cup, chopped	73	0.7

contd...

Fruits

Ingredients	Measure	Calories (kcal)	Fat (gm)
Pears	1 cup, chopped	71	0.3
Kiwi	1 cup, chopped	70	0.7
Peaches	1 cup, chopped	70	0.4
Apple	1 cup, chopped	68	0.6
Lychee	1 cup, chopped	68	0.2
Guava	1 cup, chopped	66	0.4
Strawberries	1 cup, quartered	66	0.3
Papaya	1 cup, chopped	45	0.1
Muskmelon (*kharbooja*)	1 cup, chopped	26	0.3
Watermelon (*tarbuj*)	1 cup, chopped	25	0.3
Lemon, *large*	1 no.	17	0.3

All the ingredients are arranged according to the descending order of their caloric count and the values are given for a standard cup (200 ml.) and tablespoon (15 ml.).

Dried Fruits and Nuts

Ingredients	Measure	Calories (kcal)	Fat (gm)
Coconut, *fresh*	1 cup, grated	444	41.6
Coconut, *dry*	1 cup, grated	331	31.2
Walnuts	1 tbsp., chopped	103	9.7
Almonds	1 tbsp., chopped	98	8.8
Pista	1 tbsp., chopped	94	8.0
Cashewnuts	1 tbsp., chopped	89	7.0
Groundnuts	1 tbsp.	68	4.8
Til *(sesame seeds)*	1 tbsp.	56	4.3
Dates, *dry*	1 tbsp., chopped	32	0.1
Raisins, *chopped*	1 tbsp., chopped	25	0.1
Dates, *fresh*	1 tbsp., chopped	17	0.1
Figs, *chopped*	1 tbsp., chopped	5	0.1

All the ingredients are arranged according to the descending order of their caloric count and the values are given for a standard cup (200 ml.) and tablespoon (15 ml.).

Dairy Products

Ingredients	Measure	Calories (kcal)	Fat (gm)
Condensed milk	1 cup	1027	27.5
Khoya	1 cup, chopped	595	37.3
Fresh cream	1 cup	582	60.0
Whole milk powder	1 cup	516	27.8
Paneer, *chopped*	1 cup (144 gm)	420	33.1
Skim milk powder	1 cup	371	0.1
Milk, *buffalo*	1 cup	234	13.0
Curds, *buffalo's milk*	1 cup	234	13.0
Low fat paneer, *chopped*	1 cup	214	0.0
Milk, *cows*	1 cup	134	8.2
Curds, *cow's milk*	1 cup	134	8.2
Ghee	1 tbsp.	113	12.5
Butter	1 tbsp.	80	8.9
Cheese, *grated*	1 cup (80 gm)	78	28.5
Low fat milk	1 cup	71	0.0
Low fat curds	1 cup	71	0.0

All the ingredients are arranged according to the descending order of their caloric count and the values are given for a standard cup (200 ml.) and tablespoon (15 ml.).

Miscellaneous Foods

Ingredients	Measure	Calories (kcal)	Fat (gm)
Chocolate, *dark*	1 cup, chopped	744	79.2
Spaghetti	1 cup, cooked	102	0.5
Jaggery (*gur*)	1 tbsp., chopped	69	0.0
Jam	1 tbsp.	69	0.0
Sugar, *whole*	1 tbsp.	64	0.0
Honey	1 tbsp.	61	0.0
Pasta (*fusilli, penne etc.*)	1 cup, cooked	50	0.3
Sugar, *castor*	1 tbsp.	48	0.0
Sugar, *brown*	1 tbsp.	44	0.0
Tomato ketchup	1 tbsp.	15	0.0

All the ingredients are arranged according to the descending order of their caloric count and the values are given for a standard cup (200 ml.) and tablespoon (15 ml.).

Transform Your Favourite Fast Foods into Healthy Foods

Fast food is the colloquial word used for foods with limited nutritional value. Generally speaking, foods that are high in *calories,* fat, salt, sugar and are low in nutrients are termed as fast foods or what we also refer to as JUNK FOODS.

Most of us indulge in fast foods that are not very healthy to have on a regular basis. Pizzas, burgers, french fries, bhelpuri, heavy rich curries and parathas are all foods that can lure us away from the strictest diet. An occasional indulgence is not harmful but getting hooked is. For example, when we choose an aerated beverage instead of water almost everyday or choose a cheese loaded pizza instead of a veggie pizza that's when we are heading towards steady weight gain. Look below to find out ways to turn fast foods healthy on a daily basis.....

- Substitute high fat dairy products like milk, paneer and curds with their low fat counterparts in soups, salads, gravies and desserts. This way you will get all the calcium and protein but without the fat.

- Avoid using ghee as it abounds in saturated fats which gets converted to cholesterol in our body and raises our blood cholesterol levels. Use moderate quantities of oil wherever required, adding more spices and flavourings to compensate for the flavour which oil lends to the food.

- Limit the use of cheese to minimal and as an occasional indulgence because it has a higher saturated fat content similar to ghee.

- Avoid deep fried foods. Use healthier options to make your favourite dishes low calorie. Check out the recipe of Low Fat Fries, page 65, which makes use of just a teaspoon of oil as compared to the deep fried Masala French Fries, page 64.

- Replace dry fruits and coconut in gravies with vegetable purées like cauliflower, as I have done in the recipe of Paneer Palak Koftas in Makhani Gravy, page 25.

- Restrict the use of high fat cream by substituting with low fat curds as I have done in the recipe of Low Calorie Thousand Island Dressing, page 16. You will be stunned to know that this simple substitution helps to reduce the caloric count of the recipe from 35 per serving to 10 per tbsp. To substitute cream in other recipes like gravies and sauces, use the same quantity of low fat milk mixed with a little cornflour. You will get a nice creamy consistency and none of the excess calories.

- Substitute calorie laden khoya (595 calories per 100 grams) with skim milk powder (357 calories per 100 grams) while making gravies, mithais etc. Refer to the recipes for Low Calorie Gajar Halwa, page 104, and Paneer Palak Koftas in Makhani Gravy, page 25, to see the results yourself.

- Consume fruits and their juices (without added sugar), vegetables and sprouts as healthy snack options instead of the packaged chips, farsans etc.

- To satiate your sweet tooth, choose a low fat fruit based dessert like Apple Rabdi, page 110, rather than one loaded with sugar and cream like Quick Rabdi, page 109.